Ceramic Formulas:
The Complete Compendium

A GUIDE

TO

CLAY,

GLAZE,

ENAMEL,

GLASS,

AND

THEIR

COLORS

Ceramic Formulas:

The Complete Compendium

JOHN W. CONRAD

Macmillan Publishing Co., Inc.
NEW YORK
Collier Macmillan Publishers
LONDON

To Barbara

Macmillan Publishing Co., Inc.
866 Third Avenue, New York, N.Y. 10022
Collier Macmillan Canada, Ltd.

Library of Congress Catalog Card Number: 72-90282

SIXTH PRINTING 1978

Printed in the United States of America

Contents

II GLAZE FORMULAS 90

Figures

Preface

The need for a ceramic formula book became evident to me through my experiences in exhibiting, teaching, and studying ceramics. This book is, for the most part, concerned with the needs of students and professional ceramists who want various ceramic formulas in one source. It is not only for the beginner at ceramic formulas but also for the ceramic industry and for the ceramist producing one-of-a-kind creative works. The book covers the many types of ceramic formulas that have been practically tested and used by the ceramic industry, and by potters, glassblowers, and enamelists. Few ceramists have the time, patience, or the desire to go through lengthy experiments to achieve the various formulas possible. Thus, an individual will be able to develop his own formulas based on the concepts and formulas given here.

The formulas were collected from publications and from ceramists themselves. The formulas are also based on several years of my own research in seeking the master of fine arts degree in ceramics and the doctorate in ceramics on heat fusion of glass over a ceramic opening, making ceramics for exhibits, and as a ceramic consultant for Tetasyn Tech International.

An extensive attempt has been made to give proper acknowledgment to the original inventors of the various formulas. It should be noted that many of these formulas have been so intertraded among ceramists that the original source has been lost. Others have been so altered or changed that the original source cannot be stated with assurance. Many have a composition similar to each other, and when this is the case only one is listed. My apologies to those persons whom I have not indicated as the original inventors of the formulas.

Introduction

Simply stated, ceramics is baked clay. This includes the mud pies made by little girls and put in the sun to dry. It also includes the Indian town of Taos, New Mexico, a clay monument that people have used for centuries, as well as the cuneiform tablets of the Mesopotamians and the Linear B Tables found at Crete and Pylos.

But if this were all there were to say about ceramics, it wouldn't be the art and science it is today. It wouldn't embrace the delicate and complex creations of such artists as John Mason (mural panels), Toshiko Takaezu (bottle forms), and Peter Voulkos (ceramic sculpture). And it wouldn't include such intricate formulas connected with glazes, clays, enamels, stains, and glass. The formulation of all these has lifted ceramics (in Greek it means "burnt stuff") from a potter's rough craft to the art it is today.

This book is about the complexities of ceramics. It contains a large number of ceramic formulas for stains, ceramic oxides, glazes, engobes, clays, enamels, and glasses to fulfill the needs of widely differing purposes and firing temperatures. Each chapter is headed by an introduction on the formulation, application, and, most important, the testing process. The testing of each formula is important; for example, one particular glaze will not necessarily produce the same desired results on different clays. The formulas given here have been tested by the author. For each, the chemicals and their percentages, firing temperatures, suggested usage, results of firing, color, and color code number (which refers to the color chart between pages 150-51) are given. But these formulas should not be considered infallible; each must be tested for the conditions under which it will be used.

There are many excellent books and periodicals covering various phases of ceramic formulas, and an attempt was made to select those formulas of the most interest to student and professional ceramic craftsmen. At the end of the book will be found a list of pertinent references. Several craftsmen have given the author their "secret formulas" for publication in this book. The characteristic generosity of ceramic craftsmen makes them want to share their knowledge so that others may also have success in ceramics.

I

Clay Body Formulas

Introduction

Since clay is the foundation of ceramics, understanding it and its limitations is necessary. Clays are so widespread in nature that deposits of various types are found all over the world; these various types have different properties. There are two classifications; residual clay and sedimentary clay. Residual clay is found in the same position or location as the parent rock from which it was formed. In general, this clay is the purer and less plastic. Sedimentary clay is formed from silts washed or blown down from higher levels. In general, this clay contains organic materials and is more plastic.

Many clay bodies are available to craftsmen: they are known as natural clay (as found in nature), commercial clay (compounds processed and made available by manufacturers), and individually formulated clay (compounds processed by individual craftsmen). Each clay and clay body compound has different characteristics. Earthenware is a low-temperature firing clay that is not waterproof; stoneware is a medium-temperature firing clay that is waterproof; and porcelain is a high-temperature firing clay that is hard, dense, and translucent when thin. To determine the individual properties of the clay formula and which clays would come closest to the desired properties requires testing the formulas.

Testing

The craftsman preparing to create a clay item has the desired properties of a clay in mind. To obtain a clay body that has all or most of the desired properties can be a problem. The craftsman must do research to find a clay body formula that has the desired qualities. Then he must test the clay body formula to discover the exact properties as related to the desired properties. The ideal testing is a sequence that determines several qualities of a clay body in one test.

The clay formulas tested in this book were subjected to a uniform procedure that analyzed each formula for the following characteristics:

1. ability of the clay to hold the glaze
2. fusion of the glaze to the clay
3. glaze retention of smooth surface
4. degree of transparency of the glaze over the stain and the clay
5. clay surface quality
6. percentage of clay shrinkage
7. plastic quality of the clay
8. reduction or oxidation color of the clay
9. suggested firing temperature

The simple testing sequence and procedure given below provides without complications the needed information about a clay. It can be used to test additional clay formulas.

Each tested formula was measured into 100-gram batches. Water was added to the dry mixture to bring the moist clay to throwing-on-the-wheel consistency. Next, part of the moist clay was rolled by hand into a 1/4-inch diameter rope form, then continuously reduced to the thickness of a string until it cracked or crumbled. The thinner the rope of clay before it cracks, the more plastic the clay is considered to be. The clay's plasticity is rated on a scale of 10 to 0 as follows:

10 Very plastic

 8 Plastic

 6 Adequate for hand-building quality

 4 Short (cracks easily)

 2 Dry (crumbles easily)

 0 Unusable

To determine the rest of the characteristics of the clay body, the moist clay was formed to a rectangular bar (as shown in Figure 1). The bar size is 4-by-1-by-3/8-inch thick with two line marks in the moist clay surface 3 inches apart. A hole drilled through one end can be used later to display the bar or to string several together. A 1-inch wide area of the bar was painted with a dark clay stain. When the clay dried, a 2-inch wide area was covered with a translucent glaze of the same suggested firing temperature. The dry bar was placed in the kiln and was fired to the suggested temperature.

Figure 1

Side and Top View of the Clay Body Testing

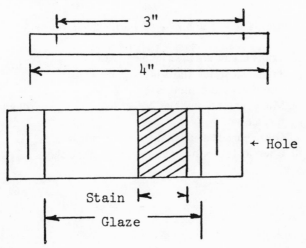

SHRINKAGE. To measure shrinkage uniformly during the drying and firing, a shrinkage scale was made on each moist test piece: two marks were cut 3 inches apart (as shown in Figure 1). After firing, the shrinkage marks were measured against the 3-inch mark of a ruler and the percentage of shrinkage calculated.

COLOR. After the clay was fired, its color was recorded. The resulting color comes from the clay itself and the oxides in the clay brought about by a reduction (low-oxygen atmosphere) or oxidation (excess-oxygen atmosphere) firing.

GLAZE. Next, a translucent glaze was painted on the clay bar to test the clay's ability to hold a glaze and the effect of the clay on the glaze. When fired, this test will show:

1. ability of the clay to hold the glaze
2. fusion of glaze to the clay
3. whether glaze retains its smooth surface
4. degree of glaze translucency
5. creation of bubbles, cracks, or craters in the glaze
6. adding of color by the clay to the glaze

All this information is abbreviated into a glaze rating scale of 10 to 0:

10 Translucent, no flaws in the glaze
 8 Translucent, few flaws in the glaze
 6 Few cracks and bubbles
 4 Many cracks, bubbles, or craters; opaque, rough glaze surface
 2 Glaze burned away, flaked off, or pulled
 0 Chemical reaction or glaze corroded the clay

Findings

The qualities desired for each clay body are determined by the temperature fired, the use of the fired product, and the technique used to construct the clay product. The information gained from the clay test will determine whether the addition or subtraction of various ingredients to a clay body formula is necessary before a clay body can be altered. For example, a clay body for a sculpture is usually coarse, heavy groged (10 to 30 percent silica sand or crushed fired clay), and porous, while a throwing earthenware is dense, very smooth, and plastic. Some possible changes for each clay body are the addition of ball clay to improve the plasticity; grog to add strength for large sculpture pieces; flint to increase the maturing temperature; and calcined clay (clay heated to remove the chemical water) to reduce the shrinkage.

The various data for each clay body formula is charted with each formula listed in the book. The translation of the information is explained in Figure 2.

Figure 2
Example of a Stoneware Clay Formula with
Explanation of Related Data

C 96* Sculptural Stoneware

Fire clay	40$^\lambda$	Temperature	C/6-9*	(The maturing temperature range for the clay)
Ball clay	30	Shrinkage	8%	(The percentage of clay shrinkage from moist to fired condition)
Grog, 20 mesh	12	Glaze scale	9	(The indication of the effects the clay has to a translucent glaze as stated in the glaze rating scale on page 10)
Flint	10	Plastic scale	4	(The indication of the clay plastic qualities as stated in the scale in Figure 1, page 9)
Grog	8	Color / oxidation / reduction	Tan brown Brown	(The clay color as a result of firing in a reduction or oxidation firing atmosphere)
Manganese dioxide	3			
	$\overline{103}$			

*The clay body number used for organization and identification.
λThe formulas listed are percentage by weight.
Note: Avoid clay thicker than 3/4".

Earthenware Clay Body Formulas   Cone/022-04

Clays fired to a mature state of hardness that will not be softened by the addition of water, at a temperature range of 1100° to 1940°F., are known as earthenware clays. Clay is an extremely abundant material formed by the continuing weathering and erosion of the surface of the earth. In its pure state it is composed of silica and alumina; additives account for the different types of clays. The earthenware type is a sedimentary clay that contains iron oxide, which gives it its rich reddish color. This clay is found in various deposits all over the world, occurs in small pockets or large surface areas in various degrees of purity, and is quite simple to mine. Most potters probably could find usable clay in their back yard or the nearest stream bed.

Clay's unusual plastic properties allowed the ancient Sumerians and Babylonians to make jars and bowls and allow contemporary craftsmen to fashion many refined shapes on the potter's wheel. While earthenware deposits are found in many local areas, not all earthenware-type clays are suitable for making ceramic forms: often different clays are blended to vary the color or to improve the plastic properties. The formulas listed in this book are of the blended type.

Unless glazed, most earthenware bodies are not waterproof because of the porosity (open) characteristic of the clay caused by low-temperature firing. The low range does not compress the clay particles to prevent water from penetrating. Higher firing ranges do compress the clay particles. However, there is an advantage to porosity: it enables earthenware to resist thermal shock, a sudden change of temperature, and thus is used to make baking utensils (providing high lead-content glazes are not used, to avoid lead poisoning).

Each earthenware formula has characteristics which will determine how the clay is used. These formulas are divided into three divisions for throwing, casting, and sculpture uses.

EARTHENWARE THROWING

CLAY BODY FORMULAS

Most earthenware throwing clays are plastic and throw smoothly on the wheel; they are sufficiently coarse to hold their shape without sagging while on the wheel; and they show little shrinkage and warping during drying and firing.

C 1 White Talc Body

Kentucky ball #4	60	Temperature	C/04
Talc	30	Shrinkage @ C/04	7.5%
Frit #2106	10	Glaze scale	9.7
	——	Plastic scale	8
	100	Color / oxidation	White (32)
		Note: Hard clay	

C 2 Talc Body

Kentucky ball #4	57	Temperature	C/04
Talc	38	Shrinkage @ C/04	6.66%
Kaolin	5	Glaze scale	9.8
	——	Plastic scale	9
	100	Color / oxidation	White (32)
		Note: Smooth, hard clay	

C 3 White Throwing Body

E. P. kaolin	50	Temperature	C/04
Flint	27	Shrinkage @ C/04	5.83%
Soda feldspar	10	Glaze scale	9.9
Kentucky ball #4	10	Plastic scale	7.5
Cryolite	3	Color / oxidation	White (32)
	——	Note: Hard clay	
	100		

C 4 Talc Earthenware

Kentucky ball #4	50	Temperature	C/04
E.P. kaolin	20	Shrinkage @ C/04	8.0%
Talc	20	Glaze scale	9.5
Nepheline syenite	5	Plastic scale	7.8
Cornwall stone	5	Color / oxidation	White (32)
		Note: Hard Clay	
	100		

C 5 Earthenware

Kentucky ball #4	48	Temperature	C/08-04
China clay	24	Shrinkage @ C/04	5.3%
Cornwall stone	24	Glaze scale	9.1
Flint	4	Plastic scale	9
		Color / oxidation	White (32)
	100	Note: Smooth clay	

C 6 Earthenware

Kentucky ball #4	44	Temperature	C/04
China clay	28	Shrinkage @ C/04	5.8%
Flint	20	Glaze scale	9.5
Cornwall stone	8	Plastic scale	9
		Color / oxidation	White (32)
	100		

C 7 Throwing Earthenware

Kentucky ball #4	42	Temperature	C/04
China clay	30	Shrinkage @ C/04	6.6%
Flint	19	Glaze scale	8.7
Cornwall stone	5	Plastic scale	9.3
Grog, medium	4	Color / oxidation	Buff-white (63)
	100		

C 8 Throwing Earthenware

Kentucky ball #4	41	Temperature	C/04
China clay	29	Shrinkage @ C/04	5.5%
Flint	16	Glaze scale	9.0
Cornwall stone	14	Plastic scale	9.2
	——	Color / oxidation	White (32)
	100		

C 9 White Earthenware

E.P. kaolin	40	Temperature	C/04
Kentucky ball #4	30	Shrinkage @ C/04	8.17%
Frit #399	15	Glaze scale	9.3
Flint	10	Plastic scale	9
Talc	5	Color / oxidation	White (63)
	——	Note: Hard clay	
	100		

C 10 White Earthenware

E.P. kaolin	40	Temperature	C/04
Talc	20	Shrinkage @ C/04	3.3%
Frit #399	20	Glaze scale	9.8
Nepheline syenite	10	Plastic scale	7.5
Kentucky ball #4	10	Color / oxidation	White (32)
	——	Note: Hard clay	
	100		

C 11 Translucent Porcelain Type

Florida kaolin	38	Temperature	C/09-04
Kona feldspar	32	Shrinkage @ C/04	5.17%
Flint	25	Glaze scale	9
Bentonite	3	Plastic scale	7.5
Whiting	1	Color / oxidation	White (32)
Zinc oxide	1	Note: Slight translucence	
	——	when very thin	
	100		

C 12 Throwing Earthenware

Kentucky ball #4	36	Temperature	C/04
China clay	30	Shrinkage @ C/04	6.16%
Cornwall stone	14	Glaze scale	9.2
Flint	10	Plastic scale	9
Soda feldspar	10	Color / oxidation	White (32)
	100		

C 13 Throwing Clay

Flint	35	Temperature	C/08-2
Kentucky ball #4	30	Shrinkage @ C/04	4.3%
Kaolin	20	Glaze scale	9.3
Soda feldspar	15	Plastic scale	8
		Color / oxidation	White (32)
	100		

C 14 White Throwing Body

Kentucky ball #4	29.4	Temperature	C/04
Talc	24.5	Shrinkage @ C/04	6.16%
Kaolin	14.7	Glaze scale	9.8
Flint	14.6	Plastic scale	8.5
Soda feldspar	8.6	Color / oxidation	White (31)
Frit #31	6.2	Note: Medium hard clay	
Bentonite	2.0		
	100		

C 15 Buff Earthenware

Kaolin	25	Temperature	C/04
Kentucky ball #4	25	Shrinkage @ C/04	8.67%
Frit #2106	25	Glaze scale	9.4
Flint	15	Plastic scale	9
Stoneware clay	10	Color / oxidation	Off-white (32)
		Note: Hard clay	
	100		

C 16 White Earthenware

Kaolin	25	Temperature	C/0
Kentucky ball #4	25	Shrinkage @ C/04	4.16
Talc	20	Glaze scale	9.
Nepheline syenite	19	Plastic scale	
Cornwall stone	11	Color / oxidation	White (32
	——	Note: Medium hard clay	
	100		

C 17 Buff Earthenware

E.P. kaolin	25	Temperature	C/0
Kentucky ball #4	20	Shrinkage @ C/04	5.33%
Frit #2106	20	Glaze scale	9.
Stoneware clay	15	Plastic scale	8.
Talc	10	Color / oxidation	Buff-white (62
Flint	10	Note: Hard clay	
	——		
	100		

C 18 Red Earthenware

Local red brick clay	80	Temperature	C/06-04
Kentucky ball #4	10	Shrinkage @ C/04	13.0%
Flint	9	Glaze scale	9.5
Barium carbonate	1	Plastic scale	9
	——	Color / oxidation	Brick orange
	100		(darker 61)
		Note: Medium hard clay, dry fully before firing	

C 19 Red Throwing Earthenware

Local red clay	70	Temperature	C/09-01
Fire clay	10	Shrinkage @ C/04	9.5%
Kentucky ball #4	10	Glaze scale	9.5
Flint	8	Plastic scale	9
Bentonite	2	Color / oxidation	Brick orange
Red iron oxide	2		(darker 61)
	——	Note: Hard clay	
	102		

C 20 Brick Red Earthenware

Local red clay	65	Temperature	C/010-03
Fire clay	10	Shrinkage @ C/04	5.16%
Kaolin	10	Glaze scale	9.5
Flint	8	Plastic scale	8
Grog 40-60 mesh	5	Color / oxidation	Brick orange
Red iron oxide	2		(darker 61)
	100		

C 21 Earthenware

Kentucky ball #4	37	Temperature	C/04
China clay	30	Shrinkage @ C/04	6.33%
Flint	15	Glaze scale	9.7
Soda feldspar	10	Plastic scale	8.9
Grog (medium)	6	Color / oxidation	Slight pink (63)
Red iron oxide	2		
	100		

EARTHENWARE CASTING CLAY BODY FORMULAS

Casting is the process of shaping a fluid material (slip) by pouring it into a plaster mold. The mold absorbs some of the water and this builds up the thickness of the clay. The excess slip is poured out of the mold when the desired thickness is obtained.

Many of the formulas listed indicate the amount of deflocculant (an electrolyte used for dispersion of clay particles) and water to be used. A deflocculant is usually added to a clay slip as sodium carbonate or sodium silicate to reduce the amount of water for dispersion of the clay.

C 22 Casting

Nepheline syenite	55.0	Temperature	C/04
E.P. kaolin	20.0	Shrinkage @ C/04	6.16%
Kentucky ball #4	15.0	Glaze scale	9.8
Flint	5.0	Color / oxidation	White (59)
Talc	5.0	Note: Hard clay, could be thrown	
Sodium silicate, dry	.2		
	100.2		

C 23 White Casting

Kentucky ball #4	50.0	Temperature	C/06-02
Talc	35.0	Shrinkage @ C/04	2.33%
Kaolin	15.0	Glaze scale	9.6
Sodium silicate, dry	.3	Color / oxidation	White (32)
		Note: Medium hard clay	
	100.3		

C 24 Casting Earthenware

Kentucky ball #4	40.0	Temperature	C/08-04
Flint	28.0	Shringage @ C/04	5.33%
Cornwall stone	16.7	Glaze scale	9.6
China clay	15.0	Color / oxidation	White (32)
Sodium silicate, dry	.3		
	100.0		

C 25 Casting Slip

Kentucky ball #4	30.0	Temperature	C/04
Talc	25.0	Shrinkage C/04	5.33%
Kaolin	15.0	Glaze scale	9.9
Flint	15.0	Color / oxidation	Off-white (6)
Soda feldspar	7.7	Note: Medium hard clay	
Frit #14	7.0		
Sodium silicate, dry	.3		
	100.0		
Water	40.0		

EARTHENWARE TERRACOTTA AND HAND-BUILDING
CLAY BODY FORMULAS

Terracotta is a heavy-groged unglazed clay most often used in hand-building techniques of coils and slabs. Coils and slabs are formed to a certain thickness and joined with a thick slip (the consistency of hand cream used to paste clay together) to form various objects ranging from a simple lidded box to a complex sculpture form. The characteristics of the clay used for building up forms are different from throwing and casting clays for it is less plastic, more open (porous) and contains a higher percentage of grog.

C 26 Terracotta

Monmouth clay	30	Temperature	C/04
Grog 20-40 mesh	30	Shrinkage @ C/04	2.8%
Local red clay	25	Glaze scale	9.6
Flint	15	Plastic scale	3
	——	Color / oxidation	Medium brick red—
	100		orange (59)

Note: Coarse grog is difficult for making small objects; use fine grog for small objects

C 27 Terracotta

Grog 20-40 mesh	30	Temperature	C/04
Monmouth clay	28	Shrinkage @ C/04	2.5%
Red clay	21	Glaze scale	9.6
Flint	13	Plastic scale	4
Fire clay	6	Color / oxidation	Medium brick red—
Red iron oxide	2		orange (59)
	——	Note: Use fine grog for small objects	
	100		

C 28 Dense White

E.P. kaolin	24	Temperature	C/04
Talc	19	Shrinkage @ C/04	3.33%
Nepheline syenite	19	Glaze scale	9.6
Kaolin	14	Plastic scale	3.5
Kentucky ball #4	9	Color / oxidation	White (32)
Frit #2106	9		
Fine grog	6		
	100		

Medium-Temperature Clay Body Formulas
Cone/03-4

Clay bodies that mature when fired at the temperature range of 2014° to 2167°F. are known as medium-temperature clays. Potters of olden days had to know the properties of this clay in order to make the best use of it. Fortunately, today the various ingredients for developing the desired properties of a clay body can be obtained from the local ceramic supplier. A clay body can be formulated to produce a casting, sculpture, or throwing type, but the most difficult characteristic of clay is the shrinkage factor, and this can range from 4.5 percent in sculpture clay to 23 percent in a very plastic throwing clay. It is a bit disheartening to throw a 20-inch vase and find it reduced to 15 inches when glaze-fired. This is why potters prefer a clay body that is somewhat less plastic, and thus shrinks less.

The medium-temperature clays shrink about 11.4 percent. When fired at the C/04 temperature range, they are not waterproof, but when fired at the C/4 range, the clay becomes waterproof without glazes. Many of these clays will make good baking utensils.

The following formulas are grouped as to throwing, casting, and sculpture clays.

MEDIUM-TEMPERATURE THROWING CLAY BODY FORMULAS

Medium-temperature throwing clay body formulas like earthenware are plastic and throw smoothly on the wheel. Most of these clays are sufficiently coarse to hold their shape without sagging while being used on the wheel.

C 29 White Clay

Fire clay	71	Temperature	C/02
Monmouth clay	18	Shrinkage @ C/02	9.5%
Buckingham feldspar	7	Glaze scale	9.6
Flint	4	Plastic scale	9
	100	Color / oxidation	Buff (63)

C 30 Stoneware, Low-Temperature

Stoneware clay	60	Temperature	C/2-4
Flint	29	Shrinkage @ C/2	12.0%
Local red clay	10	Glaze scale	8.5
Barium carbonate	1	Plastic scale	8.5
	——	Color / oxidation	Tan (39)
	100		

C 31 White Clay

China clay	55	Temperature	C/2-3
Kentucky ball #4	18	Shrinkage @ C/2	6.66%
Potash feldspar	18	Glaze scale	8
Flint	9	Plastic scale	9.5
	——	Color / oxidation	White (32)
	100	Note: Clay scratches easily	

C 32 Cream -Color Clay

Kentucky ball #4	44.7	Temperature	C/2
Soda feldspar	25.9	Shrinkage @ C/2	12.0%
Flint	14.7	Glaze scale	9
Kaolin	7.4	Plastic scale	9
Red clay	7.3	Color / oxidation	Light tan (40)
	——		
	100.0		

C 33 White Earthenware

Kaolin	35	Temperature	C/1-5
Kentucky ball #4	20	Shrinkage @ C/2	5.33%
Flint	20	Glaze scale	9.5
Talc	15	Plastic scale	7.5
Cornwall stone	10	Color / oxidation	White (32)
	——	Note: Scratches easily	
	100		

C 34 Plastic Clay

Stoneware clay	33	Temperature	C/1-5
Local red clay	27	Shrinkage @ C/2	12.33%
Ball clay	20	Glaze scale	8.8
Flint	9	Plastic scale	9.2
Cornwall stone	8	Color / oxidation	Medium tan (27)
Nepheline syenite	3		
	100		

C 35 Medium-Temperature Clay

Flint	33	Temperature	C/2
Kentucky ball #4	26	Shrinkage @ C/2	10.66%
China clay	22	Glaze scale	9.5
Cornwall stone	19	Plastic scale	9
	100	Color / oxidation	Light cool tan (31)

C 36 Medium-Temperature Clay

Flint	28	Temperature	C/01-2
Kentucky ball #4	24	Shrinkage @ C/2	5.16%
China clay	24	Glaze scale	9.5
Cornwall stone	19	Plastic scale	9
Stoneware clay	5	Color / oxidation	White (30)
	100	Note: Surface scratches easily	

C 37 Plastic Clay

Red clay	71	Temperature	C/1-5
Kentucky ball #4	19	Shrinkage @ C/2	14.16%
Fire clay	10	Glaze scale	7
	100	Plastic scale	9
		Color / oxidation	Brick red (80)

C 38 Red Clay

Local red clay	70	Temperature	C/03-5
Fire clay	17	Shrinkage @ C/2	14.0%
Kentucky ball #4	11	Glaze scale	8.0
Bentonite	2	Plastic scale	9
	———	Color / oxidation	Brick red (80)
	100		

C 39 Light Red Clay

Local red clay	55	Temperature	C/2
Flint	22	Shrinkage @ C/2	10.17%
Kaolin	14	Glaze scale	8.5
Fire clay	9	Plastic scale	8.0
	———	Color / oxidation	Brick red–tan (37)
	100		

C 40 Clay

Jordan clay	55	Temperature	C/02-5
Local red clay	22	Shrinkage @ C/2	10.83%
Fire clay	13	Glaze scale	8.5
Barnard clay	5	Plastic scale	8.7
Kentucky ball #4	5	Color / oxidation	Light brown (34)
	———		
	100		

C 41 Red Clay

Red clay	40	Temperature	C/01-5
Stoneware clay	20	Shrinkage @ C/2	8.50%
Talc	15	Glaze scale	8.5
Flint	15	Plastic scale	8.3
Nepheline syenite	10	Color / oxidation	Red-brown brick (37)
	———		
	100		

C 42 Brick Red

P.V. fire clay	30	Temperature	C/2-8
Local red clay	25	Shrinkage @ C/2	9.83%
Monmouth clay	20	Glaze scale	8.9
Grog 40-60 mesh	10	Plastic scale	8.5
Nepheline syenite	10	Color / oxidation	Brick red (37)
Flint	5		
	100		

C 43 Plastic Clay

Red clay	25	Temperature	C/2-5
Stoneware clay	25	Shrinkage @ C/2	10.33%
Kentucky ball #4	25	Glaze scale	8.8
Fire clay	15	Plastic scale	8.2
Flint	10	Color / oxidation	Light brick (37)
	100		

MEDIUM-TEMPERATURE CASTING CLAY BODY FORMULAS

Casting clays for the most part should contain a deflocculant. This helps the dispersion of the clay in a slip form and less water is necessary per amount of dry clay. Therefore, the castings remove from the plaster mold easier and shrink less because of the small amount of water used.

C 44 Translucent Clay

Nepheline syenite	38.0	Temperature	C/2-4
Kentucky ball #4	29.0	Shrinkage @ C/2	11.33%
E.P. kaolin	17.0	Glaze scale	9.6
Potash feldspar	9.0	Color / oxidation	White (32)
Flint	7.0		
Sodium silicate, dry	.1		
	100.1		
Water	25		

C 45 White Casting

Kaolin	30.0	Temperature	C/1-5
Nepheline syenite	27.0	Shrinkage @ C/2	6.5%
Kentucky ball #4	19.0	Glaze scale	9.8
Flint	12.0	Color / oxidation	White (32)
Talc	12.0		
Sodium silicate, dry	.2		
	100.2		

C 46 Red-brown Casting Earthenware

Kentucky ball #4	40.0	Temperature	C/03-2
Red clay	20.0	Shrinkage @ C/2	11.66%
Kaolin	20.0	Glaze scale	8.5
Fire clay	15.0	Color / oxidation	Light brown (38)
Barnard clay	5.0		
Sodium silicate, dry	.2		
	100.2		

C 47 Light Brown Earthenware

Kaolin	25.0	Temperature	C/1-5
Nepheline syenite	25.0	Shrinkage @ C/2	10.5%
Kentucky ball #4	20.0	Glaze scale	9.0
Red clay	10.0	Color / oxidation	Light brown (38)
Flint	9.0		
Talc	8.0		
Red iron oxide	3.0		
Sodium silicate, dry	.2		
	100.2		

MEDIUM-TEMPERATURE SCULPTURE CLAY BODY FORMULAS

Sculpture or hand-building clays usually contain more grog (crushed fired clay or silica sand) than wheel-throwing or casting clays. This aggregate gives the clay more body; thus the ability of the clay to be used as thin slabs in construction without slumping or readily collapsing. The grog also reduces the clay shrinkage, gives clay a color speckling, reduces warping and, when scraped, a coarse surface.

C 48 Sculpture Clay

Kentucky ball #4	34	Temperature	C/2-4
Fire clay	33	Shrinkage @ C/2	9.33%
Local red clay	17	Glaze scale	9.0
Grog 20-40 mesh	16	Plastic scale	5.5
	——	Color / oxidation	Buff (40)
	100		

C 49 Gray Sculpture

Plastic kaolin	20	Temperature	C/02-4
Fire clay	20	Shrinkage @ C/2	8.66%
Ball clay	20	Glaze scale	9.3
Grog 60-80 mesh	15	Plastic scale	7.4
Grog 40 mesh	10	Color / oxidation	Cream (15)
Nepheline syenite	10	Note: stony finish	
Talc	5		
	——		
	100		

C 50 Hand-Building

Red clay	45	Temperature	C/03-2
Stoneware clay	25	Shrinkage @ C/2	9.33%
Sand	15	Glaze scale	8.5
Talc	10	Plastic scale	7.0
Potash feldspar	5	Color / oxidation	Brick red (80)
	——		
	100		

C 51 Brick Red

Plastic fire clay	42	Temperature	C/2
Local red clay	25	Shrinkage @ C/2	9.83%
Kentucky ball #4	15	Glaze scale	8.1
Sand	10	Plastic scale	7.6
Red iron oxide	3	Color / oxidation	Brick red (80)
	95		

C 52 Sculpture Terracotta

Grog 60-100 mesh	32	Temperature	C/2-4
Grog 30-60 mesh	30	Shrinkage @C/2	4.5%
Kentucky ball #4	10	Glaze scale	8.2
Local red clay	10	Plastic scale	5
E.P. kaolin	8	Color / oxidation	Light brick red (39)
Bentonite	6	Note: Coarse surface	
Barium carbonate	4		
	100		

Stoneware Clay Body Formulas   Cone/5-10

A clay body that matures into a vitreous state (where the clay will not revert to a fluid condition) in the temperature range of 2187° to 2390°F. is called stoneware clay. Natural clays of this temperature range are common, but not as common as earthenware clays. The color of stoneware can range from cream to brown-black, depending on the colorants in the clay and the kiln atmosphere firing. The amount of oxygen in the kiln chamber (known as atmosphere character, it is determined by kiln design and by the method of heat production) affects the metallic oxides in the clay and this gives color to clays. For example, in a high-oxygen atmosphere kiln, iron oxide produces a buff color, while the same clay fired in a low-oxygen atmosphere kiln will be a gray color.

The plastic qualities of the clays range from very plastic, with a high percentage of shrinkage, to relatively nonplastic, with little shrinkage. Few natural clays have all the qualities that the potter requires, and thus stoneware bodies are blends of plastic clay, refractory clay, colorant, grog, and other ingredients. The combination of these materials and the stoneware firing range cause the clay to be waterproof and dense; when struck, it will give off a metallic sound. Food-baking utensils should not be made out of stoneware because the thermal shock that results when the utensil, filled with food, is taken out of the refrigerator and placed in a hot oven will cause most stoneware to crack.

Stoneware is the most popular clay with potters because of its strength and, most important, the character of the finished project. Most of these clays are light gray or dark brown in color; the gray clay has light and dark specks and the brown clay has very dark specks. These specks give the clay and glaze the subtle spotted effects characteristic of stoneware.

The formulas that follow are grouped by throwing, casting, and hand-building.

STONEWARE THROWING CLAY BODY FORMULAS

The most glamorous and intriguing process of ceramics involves the potter's wheel. This wheel has evolved from the simplest ancient Chinese wood construction to the present welded steel construction with heavy bearings and the electric power that makes it a precision tool. The wheel lends itself to ceramic forms that are unique to the character of the potter's hands on the wheel. The relationship of the impressionable soft and plastic clay to the hand shows up in the throwing marks that occur naturally on the wheel. The throwing marks are part of the ceramic form, and stoneware clay shows distinctively this manifestation. Thus, many stoneware formulas produce satisfactory throwing clays for strength and virility. The following formulas are suited for these stoneware characteristics.

C 53 Stoneware

Stoneware clay	77.3	Temperature	C/8-10
Kentucky ball #4	11.5	Shrinkage @ C/8	10.9%
Potash feldspar	11.2	Glaze scale	9.5
	——	Plastic scale	8.4
	100.0	Color / oxidation	Gray (151)
		/ reduction	Tan (35)

C 54 Stoneware

Local stoneware clay	76.0	Temperature	C/8-10
Kentucky ball #4	14.5	Shrinkage @ C/8	10.41%
Potash feldspar	9.5	Glaze scale	9.5
	——	Plastic scale	9.0
	100.0	Color / oxidation	Gray (151)
		/ reduction	Tan (35)

C 55 Fire Clay Stoneware

Fire clay	60	Temperature	C/6-9
Kentucky ball #4	40	Shrinkage @ C/8	14.37%
	____	Glaze scale	9.0
	100	Plastic scale	9.0
		Color / oxidation	Cream (30)
		/ reduction	Tan (33)

C 56 Jordan Clay Stoneware

Jordan clay	58.7	Temperature	C/7-9
Kentucky ball #4	19.0	Shrinkage @ C/8	9.27%
Flint	9.3	Glaze scale	9.1
Potash felspar	8.0	Plastic scale	9.0
Kaolin	5.0	Color / oxidation	Tan (40)
	____	/ reduction	Warm gray (103)
	100.0		

C 57 Lincoln Clay Stoneware

Lincoln clay	50	Temperature	C/8
Fire clay	25	Shrinkage @ C/8	11.98%
Kentucky ball #4	15	Glaze scale	9.0
Talc	5	Plastic scale	9.0
Flint	5	Color / oxidation	Cream (29)
	____	/ reduction	Tan (72)
	100		

C 58 Stoneware

Stoneware clay	50.0	Temperature	C/8-10
Kentucky ball #4	21.5	Shrinkage @ C/8	13.54%
Potash feldspar	17.0	Glaze scale	9.4
Flint	11.5	Plastic scale	8.7
	____	Color / oxidation	Gray (103)
	100.0	/ reduction	Warm gray, specks (103)

C 59 Kentucky Ball Stoneware

Kentucky ball #4	48.7	Temperature	C/4-6
China clay	31.7	Shrinkage @ C/6	10.83%
Flint	17.0	Glaze scale	9.5
Cornwall stone	2.6	Plastic scale	8.8
	——	Color / oxidation	Cream (15)
	100.0		

C 60 Buff Stoneware

Stoneware clay	47	Temperature	C/8-10
Kentucky ball #4	31	Shrinkage @ C/8	10.31%
Flint	22	Glaze scale	9.4
	——	Plastic scale	9.0
	100	Color / oxidation	Off-white (29)
		/ reduction	Buff, speckled (22)

C 61 Stoneware

Kentucky ball #4	45	Temperature	C/7-9
China clay	25	Shrinkage @ C/8	10.42%
Fire clay	20	Glaze scale	9.4
Flint	15	Plastic scale	9.2
	——	Color / oxidation	Off-white (30)
	105	/ reduction	Cream (29)

C 62 Off-white Stoneware (G. Hitchins, University of Illinois, Urbana)

Grolley kaolin	42.8	Temperature	C/7-11
Kentucky ball #4	17.8	Shrinkage @ C/8	13.13%
Custer feldspar	17.8	Glaze scale	9.4
Fire clay	10.8	Plastic scale	8.0
Silica	10.8	Color / oxidation	Off-white (30)
	——	/ reduction	Warm gray (100)
	100.0		

C 63 Plastic Vetrox

Plastic vetrox clay	44.2	Temperature	C/6-9
Kentucky ball #4	21.0	Shrinkage @ C/8	13.54%
China clay	21.0	Glaze scale	9.4
Fine grog	5.2	Plastic scale	8.3
Talc	5.2	Color / oxidation	Gray (8)
Bentonite	3.4	/ reduction	Gray (131)
	100.0		

C 64 Stoneware

Kaolin	40	Temperature	C/7-10
Kentucky ball #4	30	Shrinkage @ C/8	13.54%
Potash feldspar	17	Glaze scale	9.4
Flint	10	Plastic scale	9.0
Local red clay	3	Color / oxidation	Off-white (15)
		/ reduction	Gray-tan (36)
	100		

C 65 Stoneware

Stoneware clay	40	Temperature	C/7-10
Fire clay	20	Shrinkage @ C/8	12.5%
Kentucky ball #4	20	Glaze scale	9.5
Potash feldspar	10	Plastic scale	8.2
Flint	10	Color / oxidation	Off-white (28)
		/ reduction	Tan, specks (35)
	100		

C 66 Gray Stoneware

Kentucky ball #4	32	Temperature	C/7-10
Kaolin	32	Shrinkage @ C/9	12.5%
Cornwall stone	20	Glaze scale	9.0
Nepheline syenite	12	Plastic scale	8.5
Flint	4	Color / oxidation	White (30)
		/ reduction	Gray (103)
	100		

C 67 Orange-tan Stoneware

Jordan clay	31.3	Temperature	C/7-10
Fire clay	30.3	Shrinkage @ C/9	11.04%
Grog 40-60 mesh	19.3	Glaze scale	9.4
Flint	19.1	Plastic scale	8.0
	———	Color / oxidation	Orange (13)
	100.0	/ reduction	Orange-tan, spotty (27)

C 68 Gray Stoneware

Kentucky ball #4	30.3	Temperature	C/8-9
Potash feldspar	25.3	Shrinkage @ C/9	12.5%
China clay	23.2	Glaze scale	9.4
Flint	21.2	Plastic scale	7.5
	———	Color / oxidation	Off-white (30)
	100.0	/ reduction	Gray (100)

C 69 Fire Clay Stoneware

Fire clay	29.4	Temperature	C/4-9
Kentucky ball #4	24.5	Shrinkage @ C/9	11.15%
Jordan clay	19.6	Glaze scale	9.4
Grog 60-100 mesh	11.8	Plastic scale	8.0
Nepheline syenite	9.8	Color / oxidation	Tan (24)
Flint	4.9	/ reduction	Tan, specks (22)
	———		
	100.0		

C 70 Cone/7-9 Porcelain Type

Kaolin	25	Temperature	C/7-9
Nepheline syenite	24	Shrinkage @ C/9	12.5%
Flint	20	Glaze scale	9.3
E.P. kaolin	15	Plastic scale	7.0
Kentucky ball #4	10	Color / oxidation	White (31)
Cornwall stone	6	/ reduction	Gray (103)
	———		
	100		

C 71 Fire Clay Stoneware

Fire clay	64.7	Temperature	C/7-9
Monmouth clay	19.6	Shrinkage @ C/8	11.46%
Nepheline syenite	4.9	Glaze scale	9.1
Flint	4.9	Plastic scale	8.2
Grog 40-60 mesh	4.9	Color / oxidation	Gray-dove
Iron chromate	1.9	/ reduction	Brown (136)
	100.9		

C 72 Brown Stoneware

Plastic fire clay	65	Temperature	C/8-9
Monmouth clay	20	Shrinkage @ C/8	10.94%
Nepheline syenite	5	Glaze scale	9.4
Flint	5	Plastic scale	8.5
Grog 40-60 mesh	5	Color / oxidation	Off-gray dove
Iron chromate	2	/ reduction	Brown (56)
	102		

C 73 Throwing Stoneware (Weiss, Los Angeles, California)

Lincoln clay	62.0	Temperature	C/8-10
Kentucky ball #4	16.2	Shrinkage @ C/8	10.93%
Fine grog	8.5	Glaze scale	9.5
Silica	4.6	Plastic scale	8.0
Potash feldspar	4.6	Color / oxidation	Cream (28)
E.P. kaolin	2.3	/ reduction	Brown (74)
Ilmenite	.9		
Red iron oxide	.9		
	100.0		

C 74 Orange Stoneware

Stoneware clay	58.0	Temperature	C/7-9
Flint	28.0	Shrinkage @ C/8	7.8%
Local red clay	12.4	Glaze scale	9.3
Barium carbonate	1.6	Plastic scale	8.2
	————	Color / oxidation	Tan (39)
	100.0	/ reduction	Spotted orange (25)

C 75 Brown Stoneware

Fireclay	54.0	Temperature	C/6-10
Sand	28.0	Shrinkage @ C/8	11.45%
Kentucky ball #4	11.1	Glaze scale	8.9
Barnard clay	4.1	Plastic scale	8.5
Bentonite	2.8	Color / oxidation	Tan (38)
	————	/ reduction	Brown (154)
	100.0	Note: Rough surface	

C 76 Lincoln Stoneware

Lincoln clay	52.8	Temperature	C/8-10
Sand 30-60 mesh	26.7	Shrinkage @ C/8	10.42%
Kentucky ball #4	19.4	Glaze scale	9.4
Ilmenite	.5	Plastic scale	8.2
Red iron oxide	.5	Color / oxidation	Tan (28)
Manganese dioxide	.1	/ reduction	Spotty brown (26)
	————		
	100.0		

C 77 Stoneware (Alfred University, Alfred, New York)

Jordan clay	45	Temperature	C/4-9
Ball clay	25	Shrinkage @ C/8	12.19%
Flint	15	Glaze scale	9.4
Potash feldspar	5	Plastic scale	8.9
Kentucky ball #4	5	Color / oxidation	Tan (28)
Barnard clay	5	/ reduction	Brown (74)
	————		
	100		

C 78 Ball Clay Stoneware

Kentucky ball #4	43	Temperature	C/7-9
China clay	30	Shrinkage @ C/8	13.54%
Fire clay	24	Glaze scale	9.4
Black iron oxide	3	Plastic scale	9.1
	____	Color / oxidation	Gray (8)
	100	/ reduction	Brown (154)

C 79 Stoneware

Kentucky ball #4	40.5	Temperature	C/7-9
Fire clay	36.5	Shrinkage @ C/8	14.06%
Local red clay	20.5	Glaze scale	9.3
Kaolin	2.5	Plastic scale	9.0
	_____	Color / oxidation	Tan (28)
	100.0	/ reduction	Brown (154)

C 80 Red Clay Stoneware

Local red clay	40.0	Temperature	C/5-6
China clay	25.0	Shrinkage @ C/6	8.54%
Cornwall stone	22.5	Glaze scale	9.2
Flint	12.5	Plastic scale	7.0
	_____	Color / oxidation	Light brown (74)
	100.0	/ reduction	Brown (154)
		Note: Maximum C/6	

C 81 Brown Stoneware

Local red clay	40	Temperature	C/8-10
Lincoln clay	24	Shrinkage @ C/8	12.19%
Kentucky ball #4	20	Glaze scale	9.0
Sand	16	Plastic scale	8.8
	____	Color / oxidation	Brown (34)
	100	/ reduction	Brown (154)

C 82 Fire Clay Stoneware

Fire clay	39	Temperature	C/8-10
Kentucky ball #4	31	Shrinkage @ C/8	11.56%
Local red clay	11	Glaze scale	9.3
Flint	10	Plastic scale	8.8
Potash feldspar	9	Color / oxidation	Tan (28)
		/ reduction	Brown (156)
	100		

C 83 Stoneware

Kentucky ball #4	38	Temperature	C/5-6
Nepheline syenite	31	Shrinkage @ C/6	9.9%
Flint	21	Glaze scale	8.8
Red iron oxide	7	Plastic scale	9.0
Bentonite	3	Color / oxidation	Brown (54)
		/ reduction	Charcoal-brown (45)
	100	Note: Metallic surface @ C/6 plus	

C 84 Stoneware

Kentucky ball #4	35	Temperature	C/7-9
Kaolin	28	Shrinkage @ C/8	12.5%
Fire clay	13	Glaze scale	9.4
Flint	10	Plastic scale	8.3
Potash feldspar	10	Color / oxidation	Gray (151)
Black iron oxide	2	/ reduction	Brown (156)
Fine sand	2		
	100		

C 85 Tan Stoneware

Stoneware clay	33	Temperature	C/6
Plastic fire clay	20	Shrinkage @ C/6	13.0%
Nepheline syenite	20	Glaze scale	9.5
Kentucky ball #4	15	Plastic scale	8.8
Flint	10	Color / oxidation	Tan-brown (160)
Red iron oxide	2		
	100		

C 86 Throwing Stoneware

Lincoln clay	33.3	Temperature	C/8-10
Kentucky ball #4	16.6	Shrinkage @ C/8	11.46%
Silica	13.3	Glaze scale	9.4
Potash feldspar	13.3	Plastic scale	8.7
Sand	13.3	Color / oxidation	Tan (160)
E.P. kaolin	8.3	/ reduction	Brown (156)
Red iron oxide	1.9		
	100.0		

C 87 Stoneware

Stoneware clay	32	Temperature	C/8-11
Fire clay	29	Shrinkage @ C/9	14.27%
Kentucky ball #4	27	Glaze scale	9.3
Local red clay	10	Plastic scale	9.0
Fine sand	2	Color / oxidation	Tan (23)
	100	/ reduction	Brown (156)

C 88 Orange-brown

Kentucky ball #4	30	Temperature	C/8-10
Lincoln clay	25	Shrinkage @ C/9	11.46%
Hyll blue clay	25	Glaze scale	9.4
Red clay	10	Plastic scale	9.0
Flint	10	Color / oxidation	Tan (28)
	——	/ reduction	Speckled orange-
	100		brown (26)

C 89 Brown Stoneware

Kentucky ball #4	29	Temperature	C/8-10
China clay	26	Shrinkage @ C/9	13.02%
Fire clay	16	Glaze scale	9.3
Local red clay	10	Plastic scale	7.5
Potash feldspar	10	Color / oxidation	Tan (28)
Flint	9	/ reduction	Brown (146)
	——		
	100		

C 90 Stoneware

Local red clay	25	Temperature	C/5-9
Jordan clay	20	Shrinkage @ C/9	10.42%
Fire clay	20	Glaze scale	9.3
Grog 40-60 mesh	10	Plastic scale	9.1
Fire clay	10	Color / oxidation	Brown (35)
Nepheline syenite	10	/ reduction	Brown (154)
Flint	5		
	——		
	100		

STONEWARE CASTING CLAY BODY FORMULAS

When a single clay piece is to be made, the wheel or hand-building techniques are faster and better, considering the time factor, but to make a number of identical items on the wheel or by hand is tedious. The use of molds is quite acceptable to make chess pieces, dinnerware, or any extensive production.

Several books are available on mold-making. To make slip (a fluid clay), the water is weighed and placed in a large container, then the weighed dry clay ingredients are slaked (sprinkled) on the water and allowed to settle at their own speed. When all the ingredients have settled, the mixture is stirred to blend the lumps. The thick mixture (about the thickness of pancake batter) is poured through a 20-mesh screen several times to create a homogeneous and bubble-free mixture. For large cast pieces, the slip is very thick; it is thinner for small pieces. Experimentation is necessary to determine the best thickness for each slip.

C 91 Off-white Casting Stoneware

Jordan clay	39.7	Temperature	C/7-9
Kaolin	20.0	Shrinkage @ C/9	11.46%
Kentucky ball #4	15.0	Glaze scale	9.3
Flint	15.0	Color / oxidation	White (30)
Potash feldspar	10.0	/ reduction	Off-white (8)
Sodium silicate, dry	.3		
	100.0		

C 92 Gray Casting Stoneware

Kaolin	27.0	Temperature	C/7-10
Potash feldspar	20.0	Shrinkage @ C/9	14.48%
Flint	18.0	Glaze scale	9.3
Stoneware clay	17.5	Color / oxidation	Off-white (31)
Kentucky ball #4	17.2	/ reduction	Gray (100)
Sodium silicate, dry	.3		
	100.0		

C 93 Brown Casting Stoneware

Fire clay	30.0	Temperature	C/5-9
Local red clay	24.8	Shrinkage @ C/9	11.15%
Jordan clay	20.0	Glaze scale	9.3
Grog 40-60 mesh	12.0	Color / oxidation	Brown (35)
Nepheline syenite	10.0	/ reduction	Brown (154)
Flint	3.2		
	100.0		

C 94 Light Brown Casting Stoneware

Kaolin	29.3	Temperature	C/7-9
Potash feldspar	20.0	Shrinkage @ C/9	10.92%
Kentucky ball #4	15.2	Glaze scale	9.0
Stoneware clay	15.2	Color / oxidation	Off-white (29)
Flint	15.0	/ reduction	Light brown
Local red clay	5.0		(light 146)
Sodium silicate, dry	.3	Note: Could be used on the wheel	
	100.0		

STONEWARE HAND-BUILDING AND SCULPTURE

CLAY BODY FORMULAS

The construction of sculpture or hand-built pots by slab, coil, or built-up method requires a clay composition different from casting clays. Throwing and casting clays usually are of too soft a texture and will not withstand the weight, strains, and pressure put upon large constructions. Sculpture clay is more porous to dry more evenly, and heavier groged for strength.

C 95 Large-Coil Construction Stoneware

Lincoln clay	47.7	Temperature	C/8-10
Grog, fine and medium	21.2	Shrinkage @ C/9	9.27%
Kentucky ball #4	17.5	Glaze scale	9.3
Sand 30 mesh	13.2	Plastic scale	7.3
Red iron oxide	.4	Color / oxidation	Gray (23)
	———	/ reduction	Tan, speckled (17)
	100.0		

C 96 Sculptural Stoneware (J. W. Conrad, Mesa College, San Diego, California)

Fire clay	40	Temperature	C/6-9
Kentucky ball #4	30	Shrinkage @ C/6	9.38%
Grog 30-60 mesh	12	Glaze scale	9.1
Flint	10	Plastic scale	4.5
Fine grog	8	Color / oxidation	Gray (23)
Manganese dioxide	3	/ reduction	Tan, specks (17)
Iron chromate	2		
	———		
	105		

C 97 Stoneware

Kentucky ball #4	29	Temperature	C/6
P.V. clay	27	Shrinkage @ C/6	8.8%
Flint	17	Glaze scale	9.2
Potash feldspar	8	Plastic scale	7.0
Fine grog	8	Color / oxidation	Off-white (29)
Bone ash	5	/ reduction	Gray (8)
Talc	4		
Bentonite	2		
	100		

C 98 Brown Sculptural Stoneware

Lincoln clay	50	Temperature	C/7-10
Kentucky ball #4	25	Shrinkage @ C/9	11.15%
Grog 30-60 mesh	12	Glaze scale	9.2
Sand, fine	12	Plastic scale	6.0
Red iron oxide	1	Color / oxidation	Cream (24)
		/ reduction	Cream (24)
	100	Note: Rough surface	

C 99 Sculptural Stoneware

Plastic fire clay	47.0	Temperature	C/6-9
Kentucky ball #4	35.2	Shrinkage @ C/9	7.29%
Wollastonite	17.8	Glaze scale	9.2
		Plastic scale	7.0
	100.0	Color / oxidation	Brown (74)
		/ reduction	Brown (154)

Porcelain Clay Body Formulas   Cone/11-16

One of the major characteristics and beauties of porcelain is its white color and finish. This is the result of high-temperature firing and the limited number of pure ingredients. Few clays as found in nature are capable of being fired to a mature state of hardness at the temperature of 2360° to 2750°F. (though there are some porcelain-type clays that are fired at lower temperatures). The prevalent porcelain mixture is flint, kaolin-type clays, and feldspars, which when fired at this high temperature range will fuse together to a white, translucent when thin, glasslike material. For most uses, porcelain is a combination of these materials that are not found as a natural clay. While stoneware and earthenware clays can be found in nature and used directly, the correct amount of the various porcelain ingredients is important, for a small change in the percentage of any item will effect a noticeable change in the fired piece. In stoneware or earthenware, such a small change would not produce a particularly noticeable change.

Porcelain is dense and difficult to throw on the potter's wheel, for it is not plastic as earthenware or stoneware; known as having a "short" consistency, the clay warps easily; firing is costly and requires an expensive kiln; and the variety of glaze colors is limited. In spite of these limitations, there are many desirable aspects of porcelain, such as crystal glazes that are handsome and unique, the pleasing muted-reduction glazes, and the unusual translucent qualities of thin porcelain.

Most porcelain items found in the store are machine rather than handmade, and thus most porcelain formulas are for press mold, stamping, slip casting, and other commercial techniques. The formulas are divided into three divisions for throwing, casting, and sculpture uses.

PORCELAIN THROWING CLAY BODY FORMULAS

Throwing porcelain enables the clay to be shaped continuously and permanently without deforming, tearing, or slumping during application of the combined force of hand and wheel. Few porcelain clays are adaptable to the throwing process in which large size or weight is pertinent. To throw forms thin enough to have the ability to transmit light is difficult and exasperating. Most wheel-thrown pots are heavily tooled (a loop-cutting tool is used to cut away on the wheel the excess clay until the desired thinness is achieved) to reduce the thickness of the clay wall. The translucent quality for most porcelains is a wall thickness of 3/16 inch or less.

C 100 Porcelain

Kaolin	55.8	Temperature	C/8-10
Potash feldspar	24.5	Shrinkage @ C/9	17.71%
Flint	15.0	Glaze scale	9.5
Bentonite	4.7	Plastic scale	9.3
	____	Color / oxidation	White (15)
	100.0	/ reduction	Gray (104)

C 101 E. P. K. Porcelain (Carlton Ball)

E. P. kaolin	47	Temperature	C/8-11
Potash feldspar	25	Shrinkage @ C/10	14.38%
Flint	25	Glaze scale	9.6
Bentonite	3	Plastic scale	6.5
	____	Color / oxidation	White (6)
	100	/ reduction	White (7)

C 102 Gray Poreclain

Kaolin	45	Temperature	C/9-11
Potash feldspar	34	Shrinkage @ C/10	12.40%
Kentucky ball #4	11	Glaze scale	9.4
Flint	10	Plastic scale	6.0
	____	Color / oxidation	White (30)
	100	/ reduction	Gray (104)

C 103 A Variation of Wedgwood's Original Formula Developed in 1775

Barium carbonate	40.0	Temperature	C/10-11
Kentucky ball #4	25.0	Shrinkage @ C/10	13.3%
Kaolin	20.0	Glaze scale	9.3
Flint	12.5	Plastic scale	7.0
Bentonite	2.5	Color / oxidation	White (6)
	———	/ reduction	Gray (8)
	100.0		

C 104 White Poreclain

Georgia kaolin	40.0	Temperature	C/6
Potash feldspar	25.0	Shrinkage @ C/6	9.0%
Kentucky ball #4	16.5	Glaze scale	9.0
Flint	13.5	Plastic scale	6.5
E.P. kaolin	5.0	Color / oxidation	White (31)
	———		
	100.0		

C 105 Porcelain

Kaolin	39	Temperature	C/10-12
Silica	20	Shrinkage @ C/10	13.54%
Nepheline syenite	15	Glaze scale	9.8
Kentucky ball #4	15	Plastic scale	7.0
Cornwall stone	10	Color / oxidation	White (15)
Bentonite	1	/ reduction	Tan (30)
	———		
	100		

C 106 Throwing Porcelain

E.P. kaolin	38	Temperature	C/10-12
Nepheline syenite	25	Shrinkage @ C/10	14.06%
Flint	20	Glaze scale	9.5
Kentucky ball #4	10	Plastic scale	9.4
Kaolin	5	Color / oxidation	White (7)
Bentonite	2	/ reduction	Light green (134)
	———		
	100		

C 107 Flint Porcelain

Flint	35	Temperature	C/10-12
E.P. kaolin	30	Shrinkage @ C/10	11.77%
Potash feldspar	20	Glaze scale	9.7
Kentucky ball #4	15	Plastic scale	6.2
	———	Color / oxidation	White (15)
	100	/ reduction	Gray (104)

C 108 Gray Porcelain

Kaolin	31	Temperature	C/12-14
Potash feldspar	21	Shrinkage @ C/12	14.40%
Flint	18	Glaze scale	9.6
E.P. kaolin	17	Plastic scale	6.8
Kentucky ball #4	13	Color / oxidation	White (6)
	———	/ reduction	Gray (104)
	100		

C 109 Potash Feldspar Porcelain

Potash felspar	30	Temperature	C/9-11
Kentucky ball #4	27	Shrinkage @ C/10	12.92%
Flint	20	Glaze scale	9.8
China clay	18	Plastic scale	7.0
E.P. kaolin	5	Color / oxidation	White (30)
	———	/ reduction	Gray (104)
	100		

C 110 Porcelain

E.P. kaolin	30	Temperature	C/9-12
Potash feldspar	25	Shrinkage @ C/10	8.85%
Flint	25	Glaze scale	9.4
Kentucky ball #4	10	Plastic scale	6.8
Kaolin	10	Color / oxidation	White (31)
	———	/ reduction	Gray (8)
	100		

C 111 Porcelain

Potash feldspar	28	Temperature	C/9-11
Kaolin	24	Shrinkage @ C/10	14.38%
Flint	21	Glaze scale	9.7
E.P. kaolin	17	Plastic scale	7.8
Kentucky ball #4	10	Color / oxidation	White (6)
	___	/ reduction	Gray (104)
	100		

C 112 Ball Clay Porcelain

Kentucky ball #4	27.9	Temperature	C/9-11
Kaolin	26.9	Shrinkage @ C/10	15.31%
Potash feldspar	25.9	Glaze scale	9.7
Flint	19.3	Plastic scale	8.0
	___	Color / oxidation	White (6)
	100.0	/ reduction	Gray (104)

C 113 Four Equals Porcelain

Potash feldspar	25	Temperature	C/9-14
Silica	25	Shrinkage @ C/10	12.81%
Kentucky ball #4	25	Glaze scale	9.7
E.P. kaolin	25	Plastic scale	7.0
	___	Color / oxidation	White (6)
	100	/ reduction	Gray (104)

C 114 Kona Feldspar Porcelain

Flint	25	Temperature	C/9-12
Kentucky ball #4	25	Shrinkage @ C/10	13.54%
Kona feldspar	18	Glaze scale	9.7
China clay	12	Plastic scale	7.1
E.P. kaolin	10	Color / oxidation	White (31)
Nepheline syenite	5	/ reduction	Gray (104)
Bentonite	2		
Dolomite	2		
Talc	1		
	___		
	100		

PORCELAIN CASTING CLAY BODY FORMULAS

Porcelain is fired at a high temperature and this reveals every error from construction either by casting, hand-forming, or the wheel. Skill is necessary to produce forms that are lightweight and possess the translucent essence of porcelain. Extensive blending of the raw materials to make porcelain clay is necessary to produce a smooth-grained fluid for casting. Lumps or an irregular blend produces hard spots or discolored areas that are not revealed until the glaze fire. These defects are distracting under the thin glaze.

C 115 White Porcelain

Bone ash	55.0	Temperature	C/6-8
China clay	25.0	Shrinkage @ C/8	17.7%
Potash feldspar	20.0	Glaze scale	9.5
Sodium silicate, dry	.2	Color / oxidation	White (7)
		/ reduction	White (7)
	100.2		

C 116 Casting Porcelain

Kaolin	53.8	Temperature	C/10-14
Flint	25.0	Shrinkage @ C/10	12.19%
Potash feldspar	21.0	Glaze scale	9.5
Sodium silicate, dry	.2	Color / oxidation	White (6)
		/ reduction	Gray (151)
	100.0		

C 117 Porcelain

China clay	50.0	Temperature	C/10-12
Potash feldspar	29.8	Shrinkage @ C/10	11.46%
Silica	20.0	Glaze scale	9.4
Sodium silicate, dry	.2	Color / oxidation	White (31)
		/ reduction	Gray (103)
	100.0		

C 118 Casting Porcelain

Kaolin	45.0	Temperature	C/9-11
Flint	35.0	Shrinkage @ C/10	11.46%
Potash feldspar	19.8	Glaze scale	9.6
Soda ash	1.0	Color / oxidation	White (32)
Sodium silicate, dry	.1	/ reduction	White (31)

100.9

C 119 Kona Feldspar Casting Porcelain

Kona feldspar	44.3	Temperature	C/6-8
Kaolin	33.0	Shrinkage @ C/8	9.69%
Flint	19.0	Glaze scale	9.6
Whiting	3.5	Color / oxidation	White (6)
Sodium silicate, dry	.2	/ reduction	Gray (104)

100.0

C 120 Gray Casting Porcelain

Kaolin	44.0	Temperature	C/10-12
Potash feldspar	30.8	Shrinkage @ C/10	13.54%
Flint	25.0	Glaze scale	9.8
Sodium silicate, dry	.2	Color / oxidation	White (31)
		/ reduction	Gray (104)

100.0

C 121 Casting Porcelain

Kaolin	43.0	Temperature	C/8-11
Potash feldspar	23.0	Shrinkage @ C/10	13.23%
Kentucky ball #4	13.0	Glaze scale	9.3
Flint	13.0	Color / oxidation	White (31)
E.P. kaolin	7.8	/ reduction	Gray (104)
Sodium silicate, dry	.2		

100.0

C 122 Porcelain

Kaolin	40.0	Temperature	C/8-10
Kona feldspar	30.0	Shrinkage @ C/10	9.90%
Flint	26.0	Glaze scale	9.5
Whiting	4.0	Color / oxidation	White (6)
Sodium silicate, dry	.2	/ reduction	Gray (104)
	100.2		

C 123 Porcelain 4321

Kaolin	40	Temperature	C/10-13
Potash feldspar	30	Shrinkage @ C/10	11.46%
Flint	20	Glaze scale	9.6
Kentucky ball #4	10	Color / oxidation	White (6)
		/ reduction	Gray (104)
	100		

C 124 Bone Ash Porcelain

Bone ash	36.7	Temperature	C/6-8
China clay	28.0	Shrinkage @ C/6	12.5%
Flint	21.0	Glaze scale	9.8
Potash feldspar	14.0	Color / oxidation	White (7)
Sodium silicate, dry	.3	/ reduction	White (7)
	100.0		

C 125 Casting Porcelain

Kaolin	35.0	Temperature	C/9-12
Potash feldspar	28.0	Shrinkage @ C/10	12.5%
Flint	22.0	Glaze scale	9.6
E.P. kaolin	10.0	Color / oxidation	White (30)
Kentucky ball #4	5.0	/ reduction	Gray (104)
Sodium silicate, dry	.2		
	100.2		

C 126 Porcelain

Kentucky ball #4	24.9	Temperature	C/9-11
Potash feldspar	24.8	Shrinkage @ C/10	13.75%
Flint	24.7	Glaze scale	9.8
China clay	16.6	Color / oxidation	White (6)
E.P. kaolin	8.9	/ reduction	Gray (104)
Sodium silicate, dry	.1		
	100.0		

PORCELAIN HAND-BUILDING AND SCULPTURE
CLAY BODY FORMULAS

Creating sculptural forms in procelain is not a common practice because of the problems involved. Extensive time and care are required to make even the simplest hand-built forms, using refined construction techniques to produce uniform walls without thin spots, all by slow drying and firing. Because of the problems, very few sculptural porcelain formulas are available.

C 127 Sculptural Porcelain

Kentucky ball #4	64.0	Temperature	C/6-8
Fine grog	12.0	Shrinkage @ C/6	13.33%
Kaolin	11.2	Glaze scale	8.5
Fine sand	8.0	Plastic scale	7.8
Potash feldspar	2.4	Color / oxidation	White (30)
Flint	2.4		
	100.0		

C 128 Sculptural Porcelain

Kaolin	22	Temperature	C/9-10
Flint	22	Shrinkage @ C/9	11.35%
Kentucky ball #4	18	Glaze scale	9.7
Potash feldspar	18	Plastic scale	7.5
White grog, 40-60 mesh	10	Color / oxidation	White (30)
Silica sand, fine	10	/ reduction	Gray (103)
	100		

Raku Clay Body Formulas

The raku process was originally a simple technique of making the humble tea-bowls employed in the ancient Japanese tea ceremony. The tea bowls used by the tea masters in the tea ceremony were molded by hand and not thrown on the wheel. This direct, almost primitive, treatment of clay was admired by the Zen Buddhists. The rakuware is fragile, due to low-temperature firing, and is porous when new. Most rakuware is made with fairly thick walls, spouts, feet, handles, and lids.

The findings and the procedure for preparing the clay, analyzing the results of testing the raku clays, are the same as used for the clay body formulas. To give the raku clay a color, use a colorant for the clay body; to place a color on the surface of clay, use an engobe or stain. The colorant formulas and percentages to be used with the raku clay are found in the section on Clay Body Colorants and Percentages (pp. 60-61).

Raku Clay Formulas

CR 1 Raku

Fire clay	55	Temperature / bisque	C/04-03
Spodumene	40	Shrinkage @ C/03	1.1%
Talc	5	Glaze scale	9
	___	Plastic scale	9
	100	Color / oxidation	Buff (63)

CR 2 Raku

Lincoln fire clay	50	Temperature / bisque	C/04-03
Coarse grog	30	Shrinkage @ C/03	.83%
Talc	20	Glaze scale	9.2
	___	Plastic scale	3.5
	100	Color / oxidation	Buff (63)
		Note: Clay crumbles easily	

CR 3 C/04 Raku Clay

Stoneware clay	28	Temperature / bisque	C/04-01
Fire clay	26	Shrinkage @ C/03	5.01%
Grog, 40-60 mesh	21	Glaze scale	9.1
Kentucky ball #4	15	Plastic scale	7
Soda feldspar	5	Color / oxidation	Off-white (63)
Flint	5		

100

CR 4 Raku

Flint	25	Temperature / bisque	C/03
Kentucky ball #4	25	Shrinkage @ C/03	3.33%
China clay	15	Glaze scale	9.3
P.V. clay	15	Plastic scale	5
Soda feldspar	10	Color / oxidation	Off-white (63)
Grog, 40-60 mesh	10		

100

CR 5 Raku

Kaolin	26	Temperature / bisque	C/04
Kentucky ball #4	26	Shrinkage @ C/04	4.17%
Plastic fire clay	26	Glaze scale	9.1
Talc	12	Plastic scale	6
Grog, 40-60 mesh	10	Color / oxidation	Buff (63)

100

Clay Body Colorants, Stains, and Engobes

Clays are formed of decomposed rock, and in the decomposing process, the clay absorbs minerals and metals that give it its color. Iron oxides are the most common metals found in clays, and these produce buff, gray, brown, and rust colors. Traces of other metals and various minerals influence the clay color slightly, but not to the degree that iron oxides do. The clay's color can be changed by the character of firing. Oxidation firing will give the iron-bearing clay a buff-to-rust color, and the same clay as a result of reduction firing will be gray-to-brown. Natural clay can be given other colors by the introduction of metal oxides used in the form of stains, engobes, and clay body colorants. These are often used instead of glazes as a means of coloring and decorating clay. This approach gives the object a more "natural" or earthy clay look. This is especially true on sculptural and relief forms.

Stains, engobes, and clay body colorants are a mixture of clays, fluxes (used to lower the fusing-point temperature of the chemicals in the mixture), and metallic oxides. Stain is a thin coating, like water colors, that is applied to a clay form to enrich the clay color. Some red and other stains need a glaze as a protective coating to prevent the colors from burning out during the firing. Engobe is applied in a thicker coating than the stain, like poster paints, to cover or change the clay color and smooth out defects. Clay body colorants are mixed directly into the clay to give or change the clay color.

The use of additives to clay body and clay surfaces has been found in all stages of cultures. Unglazed Neolithid (300 B.C.) ceramics decorated with colored engobes have been uncovered in Asia. A more refined development of ceramics most likely started in Asia, as indicated by excavations in India, Central Asia, and the Near East. Unglazed pottery with engobe decorations was made at Susa in the fourth millennium before Christ. Geometric animal forms were used to decorate the jars and bowls. These earliest engobes are the forerunners of engobe decoration used by the most primitive ceramic-producing cultures as well as by the most sophisticated, viz., Wedgwood and Metlock.

Clay Body Colorants

Clay is the foundation of ceramics and the effects of the metallic oxides in the clay are important. Even the smallest amount of undesired oxides can influence a glaze color. For example, traces of manganese oxides in a clay body will give a uranium oxide glaze a grayed (dirty) yellow instead of bright yellow. However, the controlled colorants added to the clay body can give the fired clay richness that it may not have otherwise, and many uninteresting glazes are enriched by the spotting, streaks, or color produced in this way.

The most common colorants added to clay bodies are not expensive and include black iron, red iron, iron chromate, manganese dioxide, and coarse manganese dioxide. Other colorants, even though they cost more, when used to make small batches of clay bodies, do not increase the cost per pound appreciably. Through a testing process, the percentage of oxides necessary to produce all possible colors for a given clay can be ascertained.

Testing

Most craftsmen have several favorite clay bodies. The formulas for these clay bodies can be altered by the addition of colorants so that the craftsman will then have several color variations at his disposal. The testing of the amount and type of colorants is necessary to determine the possible colors.

The clay body colorants tested in this book were subjected to a uniform procedure that analyzed each colorant added to a clay for the following characteristics:

1. any chemical reaction of the colorant to the clay
2. the various colors possible
3. the percentage of colorants necessary to achieve the desired color
4. the color of the clay as a result of reduction and oxidation firing

Below is the testing sequence and procedure that provides, without complications, the needed information about the clay body colorants. The process has been tried and it works and thus can be used to test additional clay formulas.

The clay body formula listed in Figure 3 was weighed, mixed, and measured into 100-gram units. The various colorants were calculated in percentages, added to the clay body, and mixed with water to form a moist clay. Each clay with its colorant was rolled into two flat oval slabs 3 inches long. These were air-dried and fired to C/04. Afterwards, the resulting color and other results were appraised. The testings were refired to C/6 and reappraised for any additional change. The second slab testing was fired to C/9 in a reduction firing and afterwards the resulting color was appraised.

Figure 3
Clay Body Formula Used for Clay Body Colorants Testings

Ball clay	28
Flint	28
Kaolin	24
Potash feldspar	13
Fire clay	5
Fine grog	2
	100

Findings

The qualities desired for each clay body colorant are determined by the temperature fired, clay body formula, character of the kiln atmosphere, and percentage of colorant used. The information gained from the tests will determine whether the addition or subtraction of the colorant to the clay body formula is necessary. The colorants cadmium sulfide, antimony oxide, and selenium effected little color change. The other colorants, in general, require the same percentage of colorants to achieve the color for earthenware, stoneware, porcelain, and raku clay bodies.

Clay Body Colorants and Percentages

Colorant	Percentage	Cone/8 Resulting Color
Antimony oxide	2	Off-white (29)
Antimony sulfide	5	Cream (30)
Black base stain	6	Gray-blue (101)
Black copper oxide	2.5	Pale olive-green (pale 143)
Black copper oxide	5	Charcoal (114)
Black iron oxide	2	Off-pink (40)
Black iron oxide	5	Rust-tan (68)
Black iron oxide	8	
Manganese dioxide	3	Black (115)
Cobalt oxide	1	
Cadmium sulfide	4	Off-white (24)
Cerium oxide	5	Pink (63)
Chromium oxide green	3	Grayed green (101)
Chromium oxide green	5	Medium gray-olive (139)
Cobalt oxide	2.5	Light blue (87)
Cobalt oxide	5	Medium blue (98)
Copper oxide	3	
Cobalt oxide	1	Gray-brown (116)
Copper oxide	2	
Red iron oxide	2	Gray-brown (116)
Ilmenite	6	Buff with specks (29)
Iron chromate	6	Gray-brown (146)
Iron chromate	3	
Ilmenite	2	Gray-brown with specks (light 146)
Manganese dioxide	3	Light brown with specks (153)
Manganese dioxide	6	Medium brown with specks (146)
Manganese dioxide	2.5	
Iron chromate	2	Gray with specks (light 146)

Nickel oxide	2	Medium tan (40)
Nickel oxide	5	Dark tan (38)
Potassium carbonate	3	Spring green (124)
Potassium carbonate	7	Dark olive-green (138)
Red iron oxide	5	Medium tan-rust (27)
Red iron oxide	8	Medium brown (35)
Rutile	3	Warm tan (40)
Rutile	6	Medium warm tan (38)
Selenium	5	Off-white (30)
Uranium oxide	5	Gray (100)
Vanadium pentoxide	5	Grayed olive-green (147)
Yellow ochre	2	Buff (40)
Yellow ochre	5	Rust-tan (68)

Stains

The term "stain" in ceramics refers to a composition of metallic oxides, clays, and fluxes used under glazes or as a very thin coating on clay. Stains can be produced in many colors. The color of the stain is determined by the metallic oxides; stain compound; method of introducing the oxides into the compound; duration of the temperature and character of bisque firing; composition of the clay; duration, temperature, and character of the final firing; and composition of the overglaze.

Some stain compositions can be mixed and used directly, while others require an extensive operation to prepare them. In this process the compound is weighed out, dry-mixed in a ball mill, then fired as a bisque (calcining) firing; and then, it is wet-ground, washed, wet-ground, and dried before it can be used as a stain. In order to obtain certain red, yellow, and orange stain colors, this extensive operation is necessary.

Stains, also known as underglaze colors, are used in the commercial production of decorated ceramics and by hobbyists in "china painting." Commercial production uses the techniques of silk-screening, offset printing, transfer prints, and painting of stains on the clay to obtain the designs and photographs for the pottery, while the hobbyist primarily paints the stains directly on the clay form. In both cases, to finish the ceramic piece with a smooth coating and protective finish, a transparent or translucent glaze is applied over the stain. This coating also protects certain stains from burning out due to the atmosphere conditions during the final firing.

Testing

Of all the ceramic processes, the making and testing of stains requires emphatic thoroughness in order to achieve consistent and certain colors. This is particularly true for stains used to obtain certain yellow, red, and orange colors, which are not only the most difficult to obtain in ceramics but are also unstable in that they will burn out in firing or turn a muddy color if the formula calculation is off slightly, or if the atmosphere of the kiln firing is not correct, or if the clay is fired at too high a temperature.

The stain formulas tested in this book were subjected to a uniform procedure that analyzed each formula for the following characteristics:

1. ability of the stain to fuse to the clay
2. the resulting color over the clay and under the glaze
3. any chemical effect on the clay or glaze
4. stability of the stain color

With each stain formula is stated the suggested technique to make the stain; this was followed in the testing of each of the formulas. Each formula was weighed out into 100-gram batches and processed according to the directions of dry grinding in a ball mill or mortar and pistle; bisque-fired to suggested temperature in a ceramic cup, wet-ground in a ball mill, washed, and reground; and air-dried. The stain was painted on two clay slabs that measured 3 inches by 1 inch (illustrated in Figure 4). Over part of the stain a transparent glaze of the suggested firing range was applied. The two testings were placed in a kiln and fired, one at cone/09 and the other slab at cone/9.

Figure 4
Clay Form Used to Test Stains

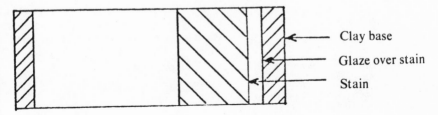

Clay base
Glaze over stain
Stain

Findings

The color of each stain is determined by the temperature, atmosphere character, and duration of the bisque firing; composition of the stain; temperature and atmosphere character of the final firing; composition of the clay base; and composition of the covering glaze. The information gained from the stain testing will determine whether the addition or subtraction of the various ingredients of the stain formulas is necessary to achieve the desired color.

Stain Formulas

S 1 White

Tin oxide	65	Color @ C/09	White (32)
Whiting	35	Color (glaze over) @ C/09	White (63)
	——	Color @ C/9 reduction	Color burn-out
	100	Color (glaze over) @ C/9	Gray (151)

Note: Dry-mix, bisque-fire @ C/6, dry-grind, screen

S 2 White

China clay	40	Color @ C/09	White (31)
White lead	38	Color (glaze over) @ C/09	White (15)
Tin oxide	12	Color @ C/9 reduction	White (6)
Flint	10	Color (glaze over) @ C/9	White (6)
	——		
	100		

Note: Dry-mix, use direct

S 3 Yellow

Zircopax	86	Color @ C/09	Yellow (4)
Vanadium	11	Color (glaze over) @ C/09	Yellow (3)
Tin Oxide	3	Color @ C/9 reduction	Color burn-out
	——	Color (glaze over) @ C/9	Yellow (2)
	100		

Note: Dry-mix, bisque-fire @ C/8, dry-grind, screen

S 4 Yellow-white

Zircopax	60	Color @ C/09	Light yellow (6)
Whiting	40	Color (glaze over) @ C/09	Yellow (4)
	——	Color @ C/9 reduction	White (6)
	100	Color (glaze over) @ C/9	Light yellow (6)

Note: Dry-mix, bisque-fire @ C/5, dry-grind, screen

S 5 Yellow

Red lead	58	Color @ C/09	Yellow (13)
Antimony oxide	30	Color (glaze over) @ C/09	Yellow (10)
Tin oxide	12	Color @ C/9 reduction	Color burn-out
	___	Color (glaze over) @ C/9	Gray (116)
	100		

Note: Wet-mix, dry, bisque-fire @ C/04, wet-grind, dry, screen

S 6 Yellow

Red lead	54	Color @ C/09	Yellow (2)
Antimony oxide	25	Color (glaze over) @ C/09	Yellow (11)
Tin oxide	19	Color @ C/9 reduction	Color burn-out
Potassium nitrate	2	Color (glaze over) @ C/9	Gray (100)
	___		
	100		

Note: Dry-mix, bisque-fire @ C/1, dry-grind, screen

S 7 Yellow

Red lead	48	Color @ C/09	Yellow (2)
Antimony oxide	32	Color (glaze over) @ C/09	Medium
Tin oxide	16		yellow (150)
Yellow ochre	4	Color @ C/9 reduction	Color burn-out
	___	Color (glaze over) @ C/9	Gray (116)
	100		

Note: Dry-mix, bisque-fire @ C/5, dry-grind, screen

S 8 Tan

White lead	43	Color @ C/09	Tan (10)
Antimony oxide	30	Color (glaze over) @ C/09	Tan (19)
Potassium nitrate	17	Color @ C/9 reduction	Color burn-out
Iron oxide	10	Color (glaze over) @ C/9	Tan (28)
	100		

Note: Dry-mix, bisque-fire @ C/1, dry-grind, screen

S 9 Orange

Alumina oxide	59	Color @ C/09	Beige (30)
Zinc oxide	24	Color (glaze over) @ C/09	Beige (28)
Whiting	11	Color @ C/9 reduction	Orange (59)
Red iron oxide	6	Color (glaze over) @ C/9	Yellow (62)
	100		

Note: Dry-grind, bisque-fire @ C/6, wet-grind, dry, screen

S 10 Pink

Tin oxide	88	Color @ C/09	Pink (47)
Boric acid	8	Color (glaze over) @ C/09	Purple (108)
Lead chromate	4	Color @ C/9 reduction	Pink (47)
		Color (glaze over) @ C/9	Pink (47)
	100		

Note: Wet-grind, dry, bisque-fire @ C/02, dry-grind, screen

S 11 Pink

Tin oxide	77.0	Color @ C/09	Pink (47)
Whiting	20.5	Color (glaze over) @ C/09	Pink (44)
Potassium bichromate	2.5	Color @ C/9 reduction	Color burn-out
		Color (glaze over) @ C/9	Gray (151)
	100.0		

Note: Wet-grind with hot water, drain, dry, bisque-fire @ C/6, dry-grind, screen

S 12 Pink

Tin oxide	62.0	Color @ C/09	Pink (47)
Whiting	32.5	Color (glaze over) @ C/09	Purple (110)
Potassium bichromate	5.5	Color @ C/9 reduction	Color burn-out
		Color (glaze over) @ C/9	Gray (100)
	100.0		

Note: Wet-grind with hot water, drain, wash with hot water, drain, dry, bisque-fire @C/04, wet-grind, rinse, wet-grind, rinse, dry, screen

S 13 Pink

Tin oxide	50.9	Color @ C/09	Pink (43)
Whiting	23.5	Color (glaze over) @ C/09	Purple (108)
Flint	18.0	Color @ C/9 reduction	Color burn-out
Borax	4.0	Color (glaze over) @ C/9	Pink (47)
Potassium bichromate	3.6		
	100.0		

Note: Dry-mix, bisque-fire @ C/6, dry-grind, screen

S 14 Red

Tin oxide	50	Color @ C/09	Red (53)
Whiting	22	Color (glaze over) @ C/09	Violet
Flint	18		(dark 51)
Fluorspar	7	Color @ C/9 reduction	Color burn-out
Lead chromate	3	Color (glaze over) @ C/9	Green (133)
	100		

Note: Dry-mix, bisque-fire @ C/6, dry-grind, screen

S 15 Pink

Tin oxide	47	Color @ C/09	Pink (47)
Flint	24	Color (glaze over) @ C/09	Pink (44)
Whiting	23	Color @ C/9 reduction	Color burn-out
Potassium dichromate	6	Color (glaze over) @ C/9	Green (135)
	100		

Note: Dry-mix, bisque-fire @ C/6, wet-grind, dry, screen

S 16 Pink

Tin oxide	45.3	Color @ C/09	Pink (47)
Whiting	29.0	Color (glaze over) @ C/09	Pink (44)
Flint	20.0	Color @ C/9 reduction	Color burn-out
Red lead	4.0	Color (glaze over) @ C/9	Green (136)
Potassium bichromate	1.7		
	100.0		

Note: Wet-grind with hot water, drain, dry, bisque-fire @ C/6, dry-grind, screen

S 17 Red

Tin oxide	45.0	Color @ C/09	Red (53)
Calcium sulfate	6.8	Color (glaze over) @ C/09	Red
Flint	21.0		(dark 53)
Whiting	20.8	Color @ C/9 reduction	Pink (47)
Fluorspar	4.4	Color (glaze over) @ C/9	Pink (44)
Potassium bichromate	2.0		
	100.0		

Note: Dry-mix, bisque-fire @ C/7, dry-grind, screen

S 18 Pink

Tin oxide	32.0	Color @ C/09	Pink (48)
Zircopax	32.0	Color (glaze over) @ C/09	Red (50)
Whiting	17.2	Color @ C/9 reduction	Flesh (46)
Calcium carbonate	16.0	Color (glaze over) @ C/9	Gray (104)
Potassium bichromate	2.8		
	100.0		

Note: Wet-grind with hot water, drain, wash with hot water, drain, dry, bisque-fire @ C/04, wet-grind, rinse, wet-grind, rinse, dry, screen

S 19 Lilac

Tin oxide	90	Color @ C/09	Lilac (light 110)
Boric acid	9	Color (glaze over) @ C/09	Violet (106)
Lead chromate	1	Color @C/69 reduction	Color burn-out
		Color (glaze over) @ C/9	Gray (104)
	100		

Note: Wet-grind, dry, bisque-fire @ C/04, wet-grind, dry, screen

S 20 Light Blue

Tin oxide	95.8	Color @ C/09	Light blue (88)
Antimony oxide	4.2	Color (glaze over) @ C/09	Light blue (85)
		Color @ C/9 reduction	Color burn-out
	100.0	Color (glazed over) @ C/9	Blue (87)

Note: Dry-mix, bisque-fire @ C/8, dry-grind, screen

S 21 Blue

Alumina oxide	85.7	Color @ C/09	Blue (99)
Zinc oxide	10.5	Color (glaze over) @ C/09	Blue (93)
Cobalt oxide	3.8	Color @ C/9 reduction	Blue (85)
		Color (glaze over) @ C/9	Blue (93)
	100.0		

Note: Dry-mix, bisque-fire @ C/8, dry-grind, screen

S 22 Blue

Alumina	76	Color @ C/09	Blue (93)
Zinc oxide	12	Color (glaze over) @ C/09	Blue (89)
Cobalt oxide	12	Color @ C/9 reduction	Blue (95)
	——	Color (glaze over) @ C/9	Blue (89)
	100		

Note: Dry-mix, bisque-fire @ C/6, dry-grind, screen

S 23 Dark Blue

China clay	72	Color @ C/09	Blue (81)
Cobalt oxide	15	Color (glaze over) @ C/09	Blue
Chromium oxide	13		(dark 81)
	——	Color @ C/9 reduction	Blue (81)
	100	Color (glaze over) @ C/9	Blue (dark 81)

Note: Wet-grind, dry, bisque-fire @ C/02, dry-grind, screen

S 24 Dark Blue

China clay	70	Color @ C/09	Blue (98)
Cobalt oxide	23	Color (glaze over) @ C/09	Blue
Chromium oxide	7		(dark 98)
		Color @ C/9 reduction	Blue (91)
	——	Color (glaze over) @ C/9	Blue (dark 91)
	100		

Note: Wet-grind, dry, bisque-fire @ C/04, dry-grind, screen

S 25 Dark Blue

Calcined kaolin	60	Color @ C/09	Blue-green (97-98)
Cobalt oxide	40	Color (glaze over) @ C/09	Blue-green
			(dark 97-98)
	——	Color @ C/9 reduction	Blue (dark 99)
	100	Color (glaze over) @ C/9	Blue (90)

Note: Wet-grind, dry, bisque-fire @ C/6, dry-grind, screen

S 26 Blue

Zinc oxide	53.1	Color @ C/09	Blue (89)
Flint	35.0	Color (glaze over) @ C/09	Black (113)
Black cobalt oxide	11.9	Color @ C/9 reduction	Lavender (107)
	——	Color (glaze over) @ C/9	Violet (119)
	100.0		

Note: Dry-mix, bisque-fire @ C/6, dry-grind, screen

S 27 Light Blue

Alumina	51	Color @ C/09	Blue (light 99)
Tin oxide	34	Color (glaze over) @ C/09	(Blue 99)
Zinc oxide	9	Color @ C/9	Blue (85)
Cobalt carbonate	6	Color (glaze over) @ C/9	Blue (83)
	——		
	100		

S 28 Blue

China clay	40	Color @ C/09	Blue (98)
Zinc oxide	22	Color (glaze over) @ C/09	Blue (90)
Tin oxide	20	Color @ C/9 reduction	Blue (92)
Cobalt oxide	18	Color (glaze over) @ C/9	Blue (90)
	——		
	100		

Note: Wet-grind, dry, bisque-fire @ C/02, dry-grind, screen

S 29 Chrome Green

China clay	65	Color @ C/09	Green (139)
Chromium oxide	35	Color (glaze over) @ C/09	Green (141)
	——	Color @ C/9 reduction	Green (141)
	100	Color (glaze over) @ C/9	Green (139)

Note: Dry-mix, bisque-fire @ C/6, dry-grind, screen

S 30 Green

Potassium bichromate	35	Color @ C/09	Green (133)
Flint	19	Color (glaze over) @ C/09	Green (141)
Calcium carbonate	18	Color @ C/9 reduction	Green (122)
Fluorspar	17	Color (glaze over) @ C/9	Green (122)
Chromium oxide	6		
Tin oxide	5		
	100		

Note: Wet-grind with hot water, drain, wash with hot water, drain, dry, bisque-fire @ C/02, rinse, wet-grind, rinse, dry, screen

S 31 Light Green

Flint	29	Color @ C/09	Light green (134)
Potash feldspar	22	Color (glaze over) @ C/09	Medium green (122)
Whiting	20		
Fluorspar	10	Color @ C/9 reduction	Green (133)
Red lead	8	Color (glaze over) @ C/9	Green (dark 133)
Calcium carbonate	7		
Copper oxide	3		
	99		

Note: Dry-grind, bisque-fire @ C/6, wet-grind, dry, screen

S 32 Blue-violet/Gray

Tin oxide	82	Color @ C/09	Gray (100)
Boric acid	9	Color (glaze over) @ C/09	Blue-violet (120)
Lead chromate	5		
Cobalt oxide	4	Color @ C/9 reduction	Gray (116)
	100	Color (glaze over) @ C/9	Gray (116)

Note: Wet-grind, dry, bisque-fire @ C/03, dry-grind, screen

S 33 Dove Gray

Flint	59	Color @ C/09	Dove (104)
Nickel oxide	22	Color (glaze over) @ C/09	Gray (116)
Whiting	10	Color @ C/9 reduction	Dove (104)
Cobalt oxide	6	Color (glaze over) @ C/9	Gray (116)
Chromium oxide	3		

100

Note: Dry-mix, bisque-fire @ C/6, wet-grind, dry, screen

S 34 Gray

Tin oxide	50	Color @ C/09	Gray (104)
Flint	20	Color (glaze over) @ C/09	Gray (116)
Whiting	14	Color @ C/9 reduction	Color burn-out
Fluorspar	8	Color (glaze over) @ C/9	Green (134)
Potassium bichromate	4		
Nickel oxide	4		

100

Note: Dry-mix, bisque-fire @ C/8, wet-grind, dry, screen

S 35 Green-brown

Zinc oxide	70	Color @ C/09	Brown (146)
Chromium oxide	30	Color (glaze over) @ C/09	Brown (155)
	—	Color @ C/9 reduction	Green (122)
	100	Color (glaze over) @ C/9	Green-brown

Note: Dry-mix, bisque-fire @ C/6, dry-grind, screen

S 36 Green-brown

Zinc oxide	67	Color @ C/09	Brown (146)
Chromium oxide	30	Color (glaze over) @ C/09	Brown (155)
Tin oxide	3	Color @ C/9 reduction	Green (141)
	——	Color (glaze over) @ C/9	Green
	100		(dark 141)

Note: Dry-mix, bisque-fire @ C/6, dry-grind, screen

S 37 Brown

Zinc oxide	56	Color @ C/09	Brown (156)
Iron oxide, red	24	Color (glaze over) @ C/09	Brown (154)
Green chrome oxide	20	Color @ C/9 reduction	Black (113)
	——	Color (glaze over) @ C/9	Black (113)
	100		

Note: Dry-mix, use direct

S 38 Brown

Zinc oxide	54	Color @ C/09	Rust (49)
Chromium oxide	24	Color (glaze over) @ C/09	Brown (73)
Red iron oxide	22	Color @ C/9 reduction	Black (113)
	——	Color (glaze over) @ C/9	Tan (36)
	100		

Note: Dry-mix, bisque-fire @ C/6, dry-grind, screen

S 39 Brown

Zinc oxide	51	Color @ C/09	Gray (146)
Chromium oxide	49	Color (glaze over) @ C/09	Brown (155)
	——	Color @ C/9 reduction	Green (122)
	100	Color (glaze over) @ C/9	Green
			(dark 122)

Note: Dry-mix, bisque-fire @ C/6, dry-grind, screen

S 40 Brown

Zinc oxide	50	Color @ C/09	Rust (37)
Red iron oxide	19	Color (glaze over) @ C/09	Brown (37)
Chromium oxide	16	Color @ C/9 reduction	Brown (73)
Alumina oxide	15	Color (glaze over) @ C/9	Brown
	——		(dark 73)
	100		

Note: Dry-mix, bisque-fire @ C/6, wet-grind, dry, screen

S 41 Black

Chromium oxide	64	Color @ C/09	Dark green (29)
Black cobalt oxide	17	Color (glaze over) @ C/09	Dark
Manganese dioxide	10		green (29)
Red iron oxide	9	Color @ C/9 reduction	Black (113)
	——	Color (glaze over) @ C/9	Black (113)
	100		

Note: Dry-mix, use direct

S 42 Black

Chromium oxide	63	Color @ C/09	Charcoal (115)
Red iron oxide	32	Color (glaze over) @ C/09	Black (113)
Cobalt oxide	5	Color @ C/9 reduction	Black (113)
	——	Color (glaze over) @ C/9	Black (113)
	100		

Note: Dry-mix, bisque-fire @ C/8, dry-grind, screen

S 43 Brown-black

Iron chromate	48	Color @ C/09	Gray (116)
China clay	48	Color (glaze over) @ C/09	Black (113)
Zinc oxide	4	Color @ C/9 reduction	Brown (155)
	——	Color (glaze over) @ C/9	Brown
	100		(dark 155)

Note: Dry-mix, bisque-fire @ C/8, dry-grind, screen

S 44 Black

Chromium oxide	48	Color @ C/09	Black (113)
Cobalt oxide	37	Color (glaze over) @ C/09	Black (113)
Flint	10	Color @ C/9 reduction	Green-black
Black iron oxide	5	Color (glaze over) @ C/9	Ultramarine
	——		(119)
	100		

Note: Dry-mix, bisque-fire @ C/7, dry-grind, screen

S 45 Black/Blue-black

Cobalt oxide	40	Color @ C/09	Black (113)
Aluminum	42	Color (glaze over) @ C/09	Black (113)
Chromium oxide	18	Color @ C/9 reduction	Dark blue
	——		(dark 82)
	100	Color (glaze over) @ C/9	Blue-black
			(dark 82)

Note: Dry mix, bisque-fire @ C/8, dry-grind, screen

S 46 Black

Black iron oxide	35	Color @ C/09	Black (113)
Cobalt oxide	30	Color (glaze over) @ C/09	Black (113)
Nickel oxide	14	Color @ C/9 reduction	Black (113)
Manganese dioxide	13	Color (glaze over) @ C/9	Black (113)
Chromium oxide	8		
	——		
	100		

Note: Dry-mix, use direct

Engobes

The ceramics produced by pre-Columbian North and South American cultures are so varied that it is difficult to generalize about them. One common point is the use of engobes to decorate their ceramic forms. The ceramic forms of each culture and region show varying colors and different uses of engobes by burnishing the clay, reduction firing, sgraffito, and wax resist. The ancient American pottery of the Mixtec country in Oaxaca, Mexico, during the late Aztec period (A.D. 1400-1521) was decorated in an attractive, highly polished polychrome motif. The motif decoration was painted in red-, yellow-, white-, black-, blue-, and brown-colored engobed slips. This well-made pottery illustrates the effective use of colored slips (engobes).

To change the color surface of clay, an engobe is often used. This is a thin layer of colored clay (a mixture of metallic oxides, fluxes, and clays) that gives color, texture, or improvement to the decorative surface of a clay form. The use of engobes reduces the need for an extensive inventory of clay bodies; it can be used as a decorative technique of painting, sgraffito, mishima, slip trailing, sprigging, and pâte-sur-pâte. Various engobes can be put on wetware, greenware, dryware, and bisqueware. The engobes must match the coefficient of thermal expansion of the base clay since the firing will cause the engobe with any substantial difference to flake off. This shows the need for testing the engobe with the clay body that it is going to be used on. The most common technique for making an engobe is to take some of the clay body and mix it with metallic oxides and water. Such a mixture is applied to the wet ceramic form and in most cases the engobe will adhere to the clay without flaking off during firing or drying. To determine the color of the engobe and its ability to adhere to the clay body requires testing.

Testing

Engobes are compounds of metallic oxides for color; clay to which fluxes are added to promote vitrification to the clay body; and nonplastic materials to regulate the drying and firing shrinkage in keeping with the clay body. The amounts of kinds of clay and other ingredients are regulated according to the clay body to which they are applied. Testing the engobe formula is necessary to determine the exact properties and color as related to the desired properties. The engobe formulas tested in this book were subjected to a uniform procedure that analyzed each formula for the following characteristics:

1. ability of the clay and engobe to withstand any flaking
2. resulting color of the engobe on the clay
3. engobe surface quality
4. suggested temperature-firing range

Each tested formula was measured into 100-gram batches. Water was added to the dry mixture to bring it to a painting consistency. The slip was painted on the surface of two clay slabs that measured 3 inches by 1 inch (as illustrated in Figure 5), that had a brown stain painted on part of the surface. The testings were placed in a kiln and fired, one at the lower and the other at the upper range of the suggested temperature.

Figure 5
Clay Form Used to Test Engobes

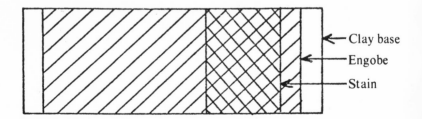

Clay base
Engobe
Stain

Findings

The choice of an engobe formula suited for use on a clay body depends upon the clay body, colorants, engobe composition, firing temperature, and atmosphere character. The information gained from the engobe testing will determine whether the addition or subtraction of various ingredients to the formulas is necessary before the engobe is used. The metallic oxides and percentages for coloring the engobe are indicated in the section on Clay Body Colorants and Percentages (pp. 60-61).

Engobe Formulas

E 1 White Engobe, Applied on Wet Clay

Same clay as being used	50	Temperature	C/05-9
Ball clay	25	Color @ C/04	White (7)
China clay	20	Color @ C/6	White (6)
Flint	5	Color @ C/9R	White (8)
	——	Note: Good coverage, apply thick	
	100		

E 2 White Engobe, Applied on Web Clay

Same clay as being used	50	Temperature	C/04-11
Potash feldspar	20	Color @ C/04	White (8)
Flint	20	Color @ C/6	Off-white (152)
Zircopax	5	Color @ C/9R	Off-white (115)
Borax	5	Note: Good coverage	
	——		
	100		

E 3 White Engobe, Applied on Wet Clay

Same clay as being used	45	Temperature	C/04-9
Flint	30	Color @ C/04	White (6)
Potash feldspar	17	Color @ C/6	Off-white (8)
Magnesium carbonate	6	Color @ C/9R	Off-white (8)
Whiting	2	Note: Translucent when thin	
	100		

E 4 White Engobe, Applied on Wet Clay

Same clay as being used	30	Temperature	C/04-9
Flint	20	Color @ C/04	White (7)
Nepheline syenite	15	Color @ C/6	White (7)
Kaolin	10	Color @ C/9R	White (7)
Ball clay	10	Note: Good coverage	
Talc	5		
Zircopax	5		
Borax	5		
	100		

E 5 White Engobe, Applied on Dampware/Leather Hard

Fire clay	50	Temperature	C/04-9
Flint	20	Color @ C/04	White (7)
Potash feldspar	10	Color @ C/6	White (7)
Calcined clay	10	Color @ C/9R	White (7)
Zircopax	10	Note: Good coverage, apply thick	
	100		

E 6 White Engobe, Applied on Dampware/Leather Hard

Frit #3124	45	Temperature	C/04-6
China clay	12	Color @ C/04	White
Flint	12	Color @ C/6	White (15)
Ball clay	10	Color @ C/9R	Semigloss glaze
Tin oxide	10	Note: Apply thick	
Potash feldspar	8		
Whiting	3		
	100		

E 7 White Engobe, Applied on Dampware/Leather Hard

Silica	30	Temperature	C/04-6
Nepheline syenite	25	Color @ C/04	White (7)
Kentucky ball #4	20	Color @ C/6	White (7)
E.P. kaolin	20	Color @ C/9R	Translucent
Borax	5		
	100		

E 8 White Engobe, Applied on Dry Greenware

Clay being used	30	Temperature	C/04-10
Calcined kaolin	20	Color @ C/04	White (7)
Potash feldspar	20	Color @ C/6	White (7)
Flint	20	Color @ C/9R	White (7)
Zircopax	5	Note: Good coverage	
Borax	5		
	100		

E 9 White Engobe, Applied on Dry Greenware

Clay being used	30	Temperature	C/04-9
Calcined kaolin	20	Color @ C/04	White (8)
Flint	20	Color @ C/6	White (8)
Frit #3124	15	Color @ C/9R	White (8)
Talc	5		
Zircopax	5		
Borax	5		
	100		

E 10 White Engobe, Applied on Dry Greenware or Bisque

Flint	25	Temperature	C/04-4
China clay	20	Color @ C/04	White (8)
Kentucky ball #4	20	Color @ C/6	Translucent
Potash feldspar	15	Note: Apply thick	
Nepheline syenite	10		
Borax	5		
Whiting	5		
	100		

E 11 White Engobe, Applied on Dry Greenware

Calcined kaolin	20	Temperature	C/04-6
Flint	20	Color @ C/04	White (7)
Kentucky ball #4	15	Color @ C/6	Off-white (8)
Nepheline syenite	15	Note: Apply thick	
Kaolin	15		
Talc	5		
Zircopax	5		
Borax	5		
	100		

E 12 White Engobe, Applied on Bisqueware

Kaolin	54.6	Temperature	C/04-9
Potash feldspar	27.2	Color @ C/04	White (6)
E.P. kaolin	18.2	Color @ C/6	White (6)
	————	Color @ C/9R	White (6)
	100.0		

E 13 White Engobe, Applied on Bisqueware

E.P. kaolin	48	Temperature	C/04-10
Potash feldspar	26	Color @ C/04	White (7)
Silica	26	Color @ C/6	White (7)
	————	Color @ C/9R	White (7)
	100		

E 14 White Engobe, Applied on Bisqueware

Kentucky ball #4	48	Temperature	C/04-6
Silica	18	Color @ C/04	White (6)
China clay	15	Color @ C/6	White (6)
Nepheline syenite	11		
Whiting	8		
	————		
	100		

E 15 White Engobe, Applied on Bisqueware

Flint	47	Temperature	C/04-9
Potash feldspar	25	Color @ C/04	White (7)
Kaolin	15	Color @ C/6	White (7)
Zircopax	11	Color @ C/9R	White (7)
CMC, dry (glue)	2		
	————		
	100		

E 16 Kiln Wash Engobe, Applied on Bisqueware

Kaolin ⎫	39	Temperature	C/04-6
Flint ⎬ kiln wash	39	Color @ C/04	White (7)
P.V. fireclay ⎭	22	Color @ C/6	White (7)
	——	Note: Translucent when thin	
	100		

E 17 White Engobe, Applied on Bisqueware

Potash feldspar	35	Temperature	C/04-10
Kaolin	35	Color @ C/04	White (7)
Flint	22	Color @ C/6	White (8)
Calcium carbonate	4	Color @ C/9R	White (8)
Zircopax	4		
	100		

E 18 White Engobe, Applied on Bisqueware

Kaolin	34	Temperature	C/04-9
Zircopax	29	Color @ C/04	White (7)
Potash feldspar	17	Color @ C/6	White (6)
Flint	17	Color @ C/9R	White (6)
Bentonite	3		
	100		

E 19 White Engobe, Applied on Bisqueware

Cornwall stone	33	Temperature	C/04-4
Kaolin	32	Color @ C/04	White (7)
Potash feldspar	30	Color @ C/4	White (7)
Flint	5		
	100		

E 20 White Engobe, Applied on Bisqueware

Kentucky ball #4	30.5	Temperature	C/04-9
Cornwall stone	30.0	Color @ C/04	White (6)
China clay	21.0	Color @ C/6	White (6)
Flint	18.5	Color @ C/9R	White (8)
	___		
	100.0		

E 21 White Engobe, Applied on Bisqueware

Same clay as being used	30	Temperature	C/04-8
Potash feldspar	20	Color @ C/04	White (7)
Flint	20	Color @ C/6	White (8)
China clay	10	Color @ C/8R	White (8)
Kentucky ball #4	10		
Zircopax	5		
Borax	5		
	___		
	100		

Egyptian Paste Clay Body Formulas

Egyptian paste is not a glaze, but rather a clay body mixed with sodium; this mixture has unusual properties that permit the sodium to seep to the surface of the clay during the drying and firing stage. This sodium, when fired at low temperatures, fuses with the flint and colorants on the clay surface to create a sodium silicate-colored glaze. Since the sodium is soluble, care must be taken during the mixing and handling. Excess handling of the objects removes the surface sodium and thus results in no glaze. In the drying and firing stage, the pieces should be placed on stilts, or in the case of beads, on Nichrome wire. Small objects can be thrown providing that little water is used to lubricate the clay during throwing.

Testing

The Egyptian paste formulas tested were subjected to a uniform procedure that analyzed each formula for the following characteristics:

1. any chemical reaction
2. ability of the paste to form a glaze
3. plastic qualities of the paste rated according to the clay plastic rating scale (see p. 5)
4. color of the fired paste
5. glaze surface quality
6. degree of hardness of the fired paste

The paste formulas were weighed out in 100-gram units. Water was added to the dry mixture to bring the moist paste to throwing-on-the-wheel consistency. Part of the moist paste was rolled by hand to a ¼-inch-diameter rope form, which was then continuously reduced in thickness until it cracked or crumbled. The paste's plasticity was rated using the clay plastic rating scale (see p. 5). The balance of the moist paste was formed into a disc shape 2 inches in diameter. Then the disk was air-dried, placed in a kiln, and fired to the suggested temperature. Afterwards the results were appraised.

Findings

The paste is short and difficult to work with; thus hand-building and throwing-on-the-wheel forms are limited to small sizes. Also the problem of the soda deposits on the surface requires the utmost care in construction and loading for the firing. Should any of the soda deposit be removed, this area on the clay will not have a gloss surface. The qualities of the paste are determined by the temperature fired, composition of the paste, and percentage of colorants used. The information gained from the paste testings will determine whether the addition or subtraction of the various ingredients to the paste formulas is necessary.

Egyptian Paste Formulas

EG 1 Dry Mat

Silica	68	Temperature	C/08
Frit # 14	18	Plastic scale	6.5
Bentonite	8	Color	White (32)
Sodium bicarbonate	6	Surface	Mat
	___	Fired paste quality	Hard
	100		

EG 2 Sprinkled Surface (J. W. Conrad, Mesa College, San Diego, California)

Soda feldspar	40	Temperature	Fire till glossy
Flint	40	Plastic scale	6.5
Kaolin	10	Color	White (32)
Fine white sand	5	Surface	Gloss and semigloss
Soda ash	3	Fired paste quality	Medium hard
Bentonite	2		
	___		
	100		

To create desired beads or forms, while still wet, sprinkle a 50-50 mixture of soda ash and borax heavily over the paste. String on wire or place on stilts for the drying and firing. Avoid touching the surface.

EG 3 Egyptian Paste

Soda feldspar	38	Temperature	C/08
Flint	19	Plastic scale	5
Kaolin	14	Color	White (6)
Fine white sand	8	Surface	Gloss
Sodium bicarbonate	8	Fired paste quality	Very fragile
Soda ash	8		
Ball clay	5		
	___		
	100		

EG 4 Egyptian Paste

Soda feldspar	37	Temperature	C/07
Flint	31	Plastic scale	5
Kaolin	11	Color	White (32)
CMC (glue)	3	Surface	Gloss
Soda bicarbonate	5	Fired paste quality	Fragile
Sodium carbonate	5		
	92		

EG 5 Egyptian Paste

Flint	35.0	Temperature	Fire till glossy
Soda feldspar	35.0	Plastic scale	5
China clay	11.3	Color	Off-white (6)
Bentonite	8.2	Surface	Gloss
Soda ash	5.3	Fired paste quality	Fragile
Sodium bicarbonate	5.2		
	100.0		

EG 6 Gloss Egyptian Paste

Soda feldspar	34.7	Temperature	C/07
China clay	21.7	Plastic scale	5
Flint	17.3	Color	White (6)
Fine white sand	7.3	Surface	Gloss
Soda ash	5.3	Fired paste quality	Medium hard
Sodium bicarbonate	5.2		
Ball clay	4.3		
Whiting	4.3		
	100.1		

Egyptian Paste Colorants

Colorants are added to the dry Egyptian paste and sufficient water is added to the batch to make the paste workable. If the mixture is too dry, add water, and if too wet, add more dry paste. The colorants listed below are suggested amounts of the resulting fired corresponding colors. More or less of the percentage of colorants given will darken or lighten the fired color.

Colorant	Percentage	Resulting Color
Burnt umber	2.0	Tan (30)
Burnt umber	5.0	Brown (27)
Cadmium sulfide	8.0	Warm white, semigloss (15)
Chrome oxide	2.0	Light green (light 144)
Chrome oxide	5.0	Dark green (144)
Cobalt oxide	.8	Light blue (85)
Cobalt oxide	2.6	Dark blue (89)
Cobalt oxide Copper oxide	.6 } 2.0 }	Blue (83)
Copper oxide	2.0	Turquoise (86)
Copper oxide	4.0	Dark turquoise (84)
Copper oxide, red	4.0	Dark turquoise, black specks (84)
Crocus martis	4.0	Grayed pink (44)
Iron oxide, red	1.0	Slight pink (109)
Iron oxide, red	8.0	Dark olive (140)
Manganese oxide	2.0	Medium purple (106)
Manganese oxide	4.0	Dark purple (dark 106)
Nickel oxide	2.0	Green-gray (light 139)
Nickel oxide	4.0	Dark green-gray (139)
Ochre	3.0	Tan (44)
Rutile	3.0	Warm tan (40)
Zircopax	4.0	White (15)

II

Glaze Formulas

Glazes have long fascinated both the ceramist and the public because of their beauty and utilitarian qualities. The art of glaze-making can be traced to Egypt, during the protodynastic period (3500 to 3000 B.C.). The soapstone steatite with a turquoise glaze appeared in this period. In many of the tombs in the burial grounds, small ceramic forms were discovered intact. Small bowls, jars, and pendants were carved out of steatite, a greenish talc rock, and "Egyptian blue glaze" was applied over them. As the ancient potters became more proficient in the use of clay, other forms were made with hieroglyphic inscriptions painted as decorations. A manganese stain was developed as an underglaze, and soon green, cobalt blue, red, yellow, and violet glazes were evolved. This is how the making and using of glazes matured.

The Egyptians, Greeks, and Romans developed practical and "rhyton" ceramics, but it is the Chinese who most influenced ceramic glazes. Ceramics was regarded as a creative art in China, and the name "china" became part of our language to describe fine dinnerware. The Chinese ceramist tried to achieve a certain ideal type of glaze, conceived as commonly dense, translucent, and with a smooth surface. The ceramists mastered the use of glaze materials, and, in turn, this mastery produced many new glazes. Several of these had unusual characteristics such as crackle, fish roe, sang-de-boeuf, oil spot, hare's fur, lustre, mottling, and celadon, to mention a few.

Not long ago, the mystery of the composition and production was kept secret. Today our knowledge about glazes has increased, but we still encounter some difficulty in reproducing certain glazes of yesterday, the formulas for which have been lost. Such glaze formulas were jealously guarded by the ancient ceramists, since they were their substance and identification. During the nineteenth century pioneering researchers of ceramic glazes introduced the principles of ceramic chemistry, and this expanded the knowledge of ceramic chemistry. These men produced valuable ceramic knowledge, developed new techniques, and published valuable information. This data and recent research have been coordinated into principles and fundamentals of glazes that are the basis of today's glaze technology. Much of the ceramic information is fragmented, however, and glaze formulas require testing under the actual conditions that will prevail when they are used. Many glazes of various temperature ranges are available to the potter. Each glaze formula has different characteristics. Earthenware, fired at low-temperature range, uses lead, sodium, or boron oxides as the principle flux; stoneware, which requires a higher-temperature firing range, has the characteristics of hard surface, variety of glaze types, is chemically stable, moderately resistant to acids or bases, uses potassium, calcium, and magnesium as the principle flux, and is the most popular with potters; and with poreclain, which needs a very high-temperature firing range, most of the glazes are transparent or translucent, as well as the most durable and hardest, and potassium is the principal flux. To determine the individual properties of the glaze formulas and which glaze would come closest to the desired properties requires the testing of the glaze formulas on the clay under actual firing conditions.

Testing

There are several commercial glazes available to the potter that will give satisfactory results. However, to accurately change the commercial glaze formula for any reason is difficult and time-consuming. It is faster, easier, often cheaper, and much more personally rewarding to make and use individually formulated glazes. All glazes for ceramic forms will have inherent limitations because of temperature, firing range, clay composition, colorants, glaze composition, and character of the firing atmosphere. This necessitates testing to determine the extent of the desirable and undesirable qualities of a glaze, its limitations, and such critical considerations as follows:

1. The glaze flow should be such that the surface will be smooth and glaze application marks blend together.
2. The surface of the glaze should be free of pinholes or bubbles.
3. The glaze should be chemically stable during and after the firing.
4. The glaze's firing temperature should mature at the suggested firing temperature.
5. The surface of the glaze should be as suggested in the "notation" concerning the glaze.

For testing, buff firing clay was made into an inverted T form about 1½ inches long. A dark brown firing engobe was painted on one side and a black stain stripe was put on the other side (as in Figure 6). All the test pieces were bisque-fired to C/09. The glazes used in the testing were weighed in 100-gram units, then mixed with water to a painting consistency before being applied to the clay. For testing higher than C/7, two T-shaped forms were used, one for oxidation atmosphere firing, the second for reduction firing. The glaze formulas dictated the firing temperature.

Figure 6
Glaze Testing Form

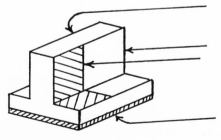

Brown color engobe, on back

Glaze over stain, engobe and clay
Black stain

Buff colored clay form

The glaze formulas tested in this book were subjected to a uniform procedure that analyzed each formula for the following characteristics:

1. ability of the glaze to adhere to the clay
2. retention of a smooth surface
3. degree of transparency over the stain and clay
4. gloss, semigloss, or mat surface quality
5. reductions and oxidation color of the glaze
6. glaze flow
7. suggested firing temperature range

After the firing, the results of the tests were appraised and recorded for each formula listed in this book.

Findings

The qualities desired for each glaze are determined by the temperature fired, the use of the fired clay products, and the clay body. The information gained from the glaze test will determine whether the addition or subtraction of the various ingredients to the glaze formula is necessary. For example, a glaze that is nonflowing, mat-surface and opaque may be desired for a sculpture form, while the glaze preferred for a teapot may be high-gloss, transparent, and with some flow. To reduce the viscosity of a very fluid glaze, flint would be added. However, a very dry mat glaze can be changed to gloss or semigloss by the reduction of flint or the increase of the fluxing agent. A transparent glaze can be made opaque by the addition of an opacifier such as tin oxide, zircopax, opax, or zinc oxide. If the opacifier is removed from an opaque glaze, the glaze will become transparent.

Earthenware Glaze Formulas   Cone/022-05

There are many ingredients that can be used to make glazes and thus numerous glaze formulas are possible. Using one glaze formula as the basic glaze and introducing opacifiers that will make the glaze translucent or opaque and substituting other fluxes will result in several glaze variations. The introduction of various colorants in varying percentages to the original formula multiples the glaze variations. The introduction of crystal forming ingredients, mat-surface forming materials, and saturated metallic oxides adds to the glaze variation. From one glaze and its possible changes, fifty or more colors or variations can result.

Most earthenware glazes use lead, boron, sodium or combinations as the fluxing agent. The yellow color of a high-lead glaze alters the colors slightly. High-boron glaze requires a longer soaking period for the bubbles to break and heal. The high-sodium glazes will affect certain metallic oxides and produce, for example, a turquoise blue, while with a lead or boron glaze the color may be blue or green. Many of the low-temperature glaze formulas listed in this book are for the bright yellow, orange, red, and other colors that are difficult to achieve. These formulas are organized into six temperature groups; subdivided as to gloss, semigloss, and mat surfaces; distinguished as to transparent, translucent, and opaque qualities; and followed by color and special-effect glazes.

The various data for each glaze formula are charted with each formula listed in this book. The data are explained in Figure 7.

Figure 7
Example of a Stoneware Glaze Formula with Explanation of Related Data

G 248* Translucent Mat

Potash feldspar	46.24	Temperature	C/6-8
Barium carbonate	23.60	Surface @ C/6	Smooth
Kentucky ball #4	11.21	Fluidity	No
Whiting	9.95	Stain penetration	Yes
Zinc oxide	9.00	Opacity	Translucent
	————	Color / reduction	Cream-white (6)†
	100.00	/ oxidation	White (7)†

Note: Temperature refers to the temperature of the glaze. Surface means the surface quality of the glaze. Fluidity refers to the fluidness of the glaze. Stain penetration is the ability of understains to show through the glaze. Opacity refers to the color of the opacity of the glaze, and color refers to the color of the glaze which results from firing in a reduction or oxidation character atmosphere.

*Each formula has a number for organization and identification.
†These numbers refer to the colors on the color charts.

CONE/022-011

G 1 Leadless

Silica	29.2	Temperature	C/020-014
Calcined borax	27.4	Surface @ C/014	Gloss
Soda ash	16.0	Fluidity	Little
Potassium carbonate	10.2	Stain penetration	Yes
Boric	5.9	Opacity	Transparent
Alumina	4.5	Color / oxidation	Clear
Zinc oxide	3.9	Note: Crackle, bubbles in glaze	
Whiting	2.9	where thick	
	100.0		

G 2 Leadless

Flint	27.8	Temperature	C/013-010
Calcined borax	19.6	Surface @ C/010	Gloss & semigloss
Potassium carbonate	19.3	Fluidity	Little
Soda ash	17.7	Stain penetration	Yes
Alumina	9.7	Opacity	Transparent
Whiting	5.9	Color / oxidation	Some white where thick
	100.00		

G 3 Yellow Transparent

White lead	90	Temperature	C/012-08
Kaolin	10	Surface @ C/08	Smooth gloss
		Fluidity	Fluid
	100	Stain penetration	Yes
		Opacity	Transparent
		Color / oxidation	Medium yellow (10)
		Note: Some cracks	

G 4 Yellow

Red lead	83.2	Temperature	C/012-010
White lead	5.9	Surface @ C/012	Smooth gloss
Flint	5.1	Fluidity	Some
China clay	4.3	Stain penetration	Yes
Tin oxide	1.1	Opacity	Transparent
Whiting	.4	Color / oxidation	Medium yellow (1)
	100.0	Note: Use over white clay or engobe	

G 5 Lead Chromate

Red lead	83.2	Temperature	C/012-010
Lead chromate	5.9	Surface @ C/012	Gloss
Flint	5.1	Fluidity	Some
China clay	4.3	Stain penetration	Yes
Tin oxide	1.1	Opacity	Transparent
Whiting	.4	Color / oxidation	Candy apple red (56)
	100.0	Note: Use over white clay or engobe	

G 6 Chrome Red

White lead	76.0	Temperature	C/012
Flint	14.0	Surface @ C/012	Smooth gloss
Kaolin	7.0	Fluidity	Fluid
Tin oxide	1.6	Stain penetration	Yes
Chromium oxide	1.4	Opacity	Transparent
		Color / oxidation	Bright orange-red (69)
	100.0	Note: Use over white clay or engobe	

G 7 Orange

White lead	72.27	Temperature	C/012
Flint	13.45	Surface @ C/012	Gloss
Kaolin	12.89	Fluidity	Little
Chromium oxide	1.39	Stain penetration	Yes
	___	Opacity	Translucent
	100.00	Color / oxidation	Orange tone (65)

Note: Use over white clay or engobe

G 8 Chrome Orange (Don Pilcher, Urbana, Illinois)

White lead	72.2	Temperature	C/012
Silica	18.5	Surface @ C/012	Gloss
Kaolin	7.2	Fluidity	Fluid
Chromium oxide	1.1	Stain penetration	Yes
Tin oxide	1.0	Opacity	Transparent when thin
	___	Color / oxidation	Bright orange (72)
	100.0		when thin

G 9 Red

Red lead	66.64	Temperature	C/012-08
Flint	17.94	Surface @ C/012	Gloss
Kaolin	8.57	Fluidity	Little flow
Potassium bichromate	4.78	Stain penetration	Yes
Soda ash	2.07	Opacity	Transparent
	___	Color / oxidation	Orange (57)
	100.00	Note: Use over white clay or engobe	

G 10 Green-black

Red lead	87.0	Temperature	C/016-012
Alumina	6.4	Surface @ C/016	Semigloss
Copper carbonate	6.6	Fluidity	Fluid
Iron oxide	.6	Stain penetration	No
	___	Opacity	Opaque
	100.6	Color / oxidation	Green-black (113)

CONE/010

G 11 Crackle Lead

White lead	48	Temperature	C/010
Flint	39	Surface @ C/010	Smooth gloss
Calcined borax	11	Fluidity	Little
China clay	2	Stain penetration	Yes
	——	Opacity	Transparent
	100	Color / oxidation	Clear
		Note: Crackle	

G 12 Yellow

Red lead	65.7	Temperature	C/010
White lead	15.0	Surface @ C/010	Gloss
Flint	10.1	Fluidity	Fluid
China clay	4.7	Stain penetration	Yes
Boric acid	4.5	Opacity	Transparent
	——	Color / oxidation	Yellow (1)
	100.0	Note: Some cracks	

G 13 Newcomb Red

Red lead	79.17	Temperature	C/010-08
Flint	8.33	Surface @ C/010	Semigloss
Chromium oxide	6.25	Fluidity	None
Kaolin	4.51	Stain penetration	Yes
Titanium oxide	1.74	Opacity	Transparent
	——	Color / oxidation	Orange-red (71)
	100.00	Note: Use over white engobe	

G 14 Orange

Red lead	70.0	Temperature	C/010
Flint	11.0	Surface @ C/010	Smooth gloss
China clay	5.4	Fluidity	Some
Chromium oxide	4.4	Stain penetration	Darks show
Soda feldspar	3.9	Opacity	Translucent
Tin oxide	2.7	Color / oxidation	Orange-red (69)
Whiting	2.6	Note: Use over white engobe	
	100.0		

G 15 Chrome Red

White lead	61.8	Temperature	C/010-08
Flint	18.2	Surface @ C/08	Gloss
Kaolin	9.1	Fluidity	Little
Potassium bichromate	4.5	Stain penetration	None
Soda ash	3.9	Opacity	Opaque
Tin oxide	2.5	Color / oxidation	Ochre-orange with red marbling (36)
	100.0		

G 16 Chrome-Tin

White lead	64.5	Temperature	C/010
Flint	19.1	Surface @ C/010	Gloss
Kaolin	9.4	Fluidity	Little
Tin oxide	3.9	Stain penetration	Darks show
Soda ash	1.9	Opacity	Opaque
Chromium oxide	.7	Color / oxidation	Orange (65)
Lead chromate	.5		
	100.0		

G 17 Flame Red

Red lead	60.5	Temperature	C/010
Lead chromate	13.0	Surface @ C/010	Gloss
Flint	11.5	Fluidity	Some
China clay	5.0	Stain penetration	Yes
Soda feldspar	3.5	Opacity	Transparent
Zinc oxide	3.0	Color / oxidation	Orange-red (68)
Chromium oxide	2.0	Note: Bubbles where thick	
Tin oxide	1.5		
	100.0		

G 18 Chrome Red

Red lead	75.67	Temperature	C/010
Potash feldspar	10.19	Surface @C/010	Mat, crystalline
Chromium oxide	5.58	Fluidity	None
Flint	4.70	Stain penetration	Darks show
Barium carbonate	3.86	Opacity	Translucent
	100.00	Color / oxidation	Bright, true red (55)
		Note: Use on white engobe, try 5% whiting	

G 19 Red

Red lead	75	Temperature	C/010
Soda feldspar	10	Surface @ C/010	Mat, crystaline
Chromium oxide	6	Fluidity	None
Flint	5	Stain penetration	Darks show
Barium carbonate	4	Opacity	Translucent
	___	Color / oxidation	True red (54)
	100	Note: Use on white engobe	

G 20 Coral Red

Red lead	72	Temperature	C/010
Flint	12	Surface @ C/010	Semigloss
China clay	5	Fluidity	Some
Tin oxide	4	Stain penetration	Darks show
Chromium oxide	4	Opacity	Translucent
Whiting	3	Color / oxidation	Coral red (56)
	___	Note: Apply on white clay	
	100		

CONE/08

G 21 Gloss Lead

White lead	55.0	Temperature	C/08
Soda feldspar	21.4	Surface @ C/08	Gloss
Flint	17.0	Fluidity	Some
Whiting	4.6	Stain penetration	Yes
Zinc oxide	1.2	Opacity	Translucent
Kaolin	1.8	Color / oxidation	Slight yellow (4)
	———	Note: Hold temperature at C/08	
	100.0		

G 22 Lead

White lead	57.0	Temperature	C/08
Kona feldspar	19.3	Surface @ C/08	Gloss
Flint	18.0	Fluidity	Little
Kaolin	2.7	Stain penetration	Yes
Whiting	2.4	Opacity	Transparent
Tin oxide	.6	Color / oxidation	Off-white (3)
	———	Note: Hold temperature at C/08 for	
	100.0	bubbles to break	

G 23 Lead Colemanite

White lead	54	Temperature	C/08-04
Kona feldspar	18	Surface @ C/04	Gloss
Flint	17	Fluidity	Little
Colemanite	5	Stain penetration	Yes
Whiting	3	Opacity	Transparent
Kaolin	3	Color / oxidation	Clear
	———	Note: Some cracks	
	100		

G 24 Raw Lead

White lead	48	Temperature	C/08-04
Flint	20	Surface @ C/06	Gloss
Tin oxide	10	Fluidity	Some
Whiting	7	Stain penetration	Yes
E.P. kaolin	6	Opacity	Translucent
Calcined kaolin	5	Color / oxidation	Whitish (64)
Zinc oxide	4		
	100		

G 25 Colemanite

Oxford spar	39	Temperature	C/08-06
Colemanite	33	Surface @ C/06	Semigloss
Flint	13	Fluidity	None
Barium carbonate	11	Stain penetration	Yes
Zinc oxide	4	Opacity	Translucent
		Color / oxidation	Slight white (6)
	100	Note: Some cracks	

G 26 Transparent

White lead	28.32	Temperature	C/08-02
Borax	22.78	Surface @ C/08	Gloss and semigloss
Flint	18.81	Fluidity	None
Soda feldspar	18.36	Stain penetration	Yes
Calcined kaolin	5.53	Opacity	Transparent
Whiting	3.32	Color / oxidation	Clear and white areas
Kaolin	2.88	Note: Apply medium to thick	
	100.00		

G 27 Light Yellow

White lead	51.0	Temperature	C/08-04
Soda feldspar	27.0	Surface @ C/06	Mat
Whiting	9.0	Fluidity	None
E.P. kaolin	4.5	Stain penetration	Yes
Calcined kaolin	4.0	Opacity	Translucent
Flint	2.0	Color / oxidation	Light yellow (3)
Tin oxide	1.5	Note: Some cracks	
	99.0		

G 28 Transparent Yellow

Red lead	58	Temperature	C/08
Silica	35	Surface @ C/08	Smooth gloss
Kaolin	7	Fluidity	Little
		Stain penetration	Yes
	100	Opacity	Transparent
		Color / oxidation	Yellow (1)
		Note: Some cracks	

G 29 Chrome Orange

White lead	66.2	Temperature	C/08-06
Soda feldspar	17.7	Surface @ C/06	Semigloss
Flint	5.9	Fluidity	None
China clay	4.0	Stain penetration	Yes
Whiting	3.2	Opacity	Transparent
Chromium oxide	3.0	Color / oxidation	Orange (72)
Glue (C.M.C.)	1.0	Note: Use white engobe or clay	
	101.0		

G 30 Chromium Red

Red lead	65.3	Temperature	C/08-07
Flint	17.9	Surface @ C/08	Smooth gloss
Kaolin	8.5	Fluidity	Fluid
Potassium bichromate	4.7	Stain penetration	Yes
Soda ash	2.3	Opacity	Transparent
Tin oxide	1.3	Color / oxidation	Yellow-orange (10)
	___	Note: Some cracks	
	100.0		

G 31 Red

White lead	70.81	Temperature	C/08-05
Flint	10.90	Surface @ C/08	Gloss, semigloss
China clay	9.39	Fluidity	None
Chromium oxide	5.47	Stain penetration	No
Tin oxide	2.43	Opacity	Opaque
	___	Color / oxidation	Blood red (34)
	99.00	Note: Grind glaze, apply thick	

G 32 Orange-brown

Red lead	57.0	Temperature	C/08
Flint	19.5	Surface @ C/08	Gloss
Borax	14.0	Fluidity	Fluid
Zinc oxide	5.0	Stain penetration	Yes
Red iron	4.5	Opacity	Translucent
	___	Color / oxidation	Orange-brown (20)
	100.0		

G 33 Purple-brown (J. W. Conrad, Mesa College, San Diego, California)

Red lead	53.6	Temperature	C/08
Flint	18.2	Surface @ C/08	Gloss
Red iron oxide	14.7	Fluidity	None
Borax	13.5	Stain penetration	None
	___	Opacity	Opaque
	100.0	Color / oxidation	Dark purple-brown (50)

CONE/06

G 34 Yellow-white

White lead	60	Temperature	C/06
Flint	28	Surface @ C/06	Smooth gloss
Kaolin	12	Fluidity	Fluid
	———	Stain penetration	Yes
	100	Opacity	Transparent
		Color / oxidation	Yellow where thick
			(4)

Note: Some cracks

G 35 Bright Gloss

White lead	53.39	Temperature	C/06
Soda feldspar	22.71	Surface @ C/06	Gloss
Flint	12.68	Fluidity	Some
Kaolin	5.90	Stain penetration	Yes
Whiting	5.32	Opacity	Transparent
	———	Color / oxidation	Slight yellow (5)
	100.00	Note: Some cracks	

G 36 Transparent

Soda feldspar	45	Temperature	C/06
Colemanite	30	Surface @ C/06	Gloss
Flint	10	Fluidity	None
Barium carbonate	6	Stain penetration	Yes
Zinc oxide	5	Opacity	Transparent
China clay	4	Color / oxidation	Clear
	———	Note: Some cracks	
	100		

G 37 Lead, Slight Yellow

White lead	61	Temperature	C/06
Flint	27	Surface @ C/06	Gloss
China clay	10	Fluidity	None
Bentonite	2	Stain penetration	Yes
	___	Opacity	Translucent
	100	Color / oxidation	Slight yellow (4)

G 38 Gloss

Soda feldspar	57.6	Temperature	C/06
Colemanite	26.3	Surface @ C/06	Semigloss/gloss
Zinc oxide	9.0	Fluidity	Little
Flint	6.6	Stain penetration	Yes
Whiting	.5	Opacity	Translucent
	___	Color / oxidation	Whitish (7)
	100.0	Note: Some cracks	

G 39 Transparent Gloss

Borax	30.0	Temperature	C/06-05
Soda feldspar	27.7	Surface @ C/06	Gloss
White lead	20.3	Fluidity	Some
Flint	6.4	Stain penetration	Yes
Whiting	5.2	Opacity	Translucent
Kaolin	5.2	Color / oxidation	Whitish (6)
Tin oxide	4.2	Note: Some cracks	
	___		
	99.0		

G 40 Translucent

Flint	30.20	Temperature	C/06-02
Borax	25.50	Surface @ C/06	Gloss
White lead	13.42	Fluidity	None
Soda feldspar	9.06	Stain penetration	Some
Tin oxide	7.72	Opacity	Translucent, thin
Soda ash	6.71		Opaque, thick
Calcined clay	4.03	Color / oxidation	White (48)
Kaolin	3.36		
	100.00		

G 41 Bright Glaze

White lead	55	Temperature	C/06
Soda feldspar	18	Surface @ C/06	Semigloss
Flint	14	Fluidity	None
Whiting	8	Stain penetration	Yes
Kaolin	4	Opacity	Transparent
Tin oxide	1	Color / oxidation	Very slight yellow (5)
	100	Note: Some cracks	

G 42 Lead

White lead	49	Temperature	C/06
Soda feldspar	17	Surface @ C/06	Semigloss
Flint	16	Fluidity	Some
Whiting	9	Stain penetration	Yes
Kaolin	8	Opacity	Translucent
Tin oxide	1	Color / oxidation	Slight yellow (5)
	100	Note: Some cracks, hold temperature at C/06 to break bubbles	

G 43 White Semigloss

Flint	43.4	Temperature	C/06-05
Soda feldspar	14.3	Surface @ C/06	Semigloss
Cryolite	14.2	Fluidity	Little
Lithium carbonate	9.6	Stain penetration	Darks show
Bone ash	8.3	Opacity	Translucent
Whiting	6.4	Color / oxidation	White (32)
China clay	3.8	Note: Some cracks	
	100.0		

G 44 Semimat

White lead	45	Temperature	C/06-05
Soda feldspar	20	Surface @ C/06	Semimat
Flint	17	Fluidity	None
Whiting	11	Stain penetration	Darks show
Kaolin	7	Opacity	Translucent
	____	Color / oxidation	Light yellow (4)
	100	Note: Some cracks	

G 45 Lead Gloss

White lead	78	Temperature	C/06
Whiting	13	Surface @ C/06	Gloss
Kaolin	9	Fluidity	Fluid
	____	Stain penetration	Yes
	100	Opacity	Transparent
		Color / oxidation	Light yellow (2)
		Note: Some cracks	

G 46 Mat

White lead	64.4	Temperature	C/06
Soda feldspar	18.3	Surface @ C/06	Mat
Barium carbonate	9.6	Fluidity	None
E.P. kaolin	3.9	Stain penetration	Yes
Cornwall stone	3.8	Opacity	Translucent
	____	Color / oxidation	Slight cream (4)
	100.0		

G 47 Gloss Yellow

White lead	61.77	Temperature	C/06-03
Flint	26.47	Surface @ C/06	Gloss
Kaolin	9.80	Fluidity	Some
Bentonite	1.96	Stain penetration	Yes
	——	Opacity	Transparent
	100.00	Color / oxidation	Yellow (1)
		Note: Some cracks	

G 48 Uranium Orange

Red lead	53	Temperature	C/06
Uranium oxide	19	Surface @ C/06	Gloss
Flint	18	Fluidity	Some
Soda feldspar	10	Stain penetration	Yes
	——	Opacity	Transparent
	100	Color / oxidation	Bright orange (69)
		Note: Some cracks, use over white clay	

G 49 Orange Chromate

White lead	61.5	Temperature	C/06
Soda feldspar	17.4	Surface @ C/06	Mat
Barium carbonate	9.2	Fluidity	Some
Lead chromate	4.6	Stain penetration	Darks show
E.P. kaolin	3.7	Opacity	Translucent
Cornwall stone	3.6	Color / oxidation	Orange (58)
	——	Note: Use on white clay	
	100.0		

G 50 Orange-red

White lead	71.23	Temperature	C/06-04
Flint	16.05	Surface @ C/06	Gloss
Soda feldspar	8.71	Fluidity	Fluid
Kaolin	2.06	Stain penetration	Yes
Chromium oxide	1.95	Opacity	Transparent, thin
			Translucent, thick
	——		
	100.00	Color / oxidation	Orange-red (65)
		Note: Use over white clay	

G 51 Red

White lead	61.5	Temperature	C/06
Soda feldspar	17.4	Surface @ C/06	Mat
Barium carbonate	9.2	Fluidity	Some
Potassium bichromate	4.6	Stain penetration	Darks show
Cornwall stone	3.7	Opacity	Opaque
E.P. kaolin	3.6	Color / oxidation	Red (68)
	100.0	Note: Use over white clay	

G 52 Aventurine

Flint	39.7	Temperature	C/06-05
Borax	38.8	Surface @ C/06	Semigloss
Red iron oxide	15.2	Fluidity	Little
Boric acid	2.7	Stain penetration	None
Barium carbonate	2.2	Opacity	Opaque
Kaolin	1.4	Color / oxidation	Aventurine (dark 50), purple-brown with gold specks
	100.0		

CONE/05

G 53 Transparent

Lead, red	62	Temperature	C/05-03
China clay	20	Surface @ C/05	Gloss
Flint	18	Fluidity	Some
		Stain penetration	Yes
	100	Opacity	Transparent
		Color / oxidation	Clear, slight yellow
		Note: Some cracks where thick	

G 54 Transparent Gloss

Borax	32	Temperature	C/05-03
Soda feldspar	20	Surface @ C/05	Gloss
Flint	20	Fluidity	Some
Soda ash	16	Stain penetration	Yes
Whiting	7	Opacity	Transparent
China clay	5	Color / oxidation	Clear
	——	Note: Apply thick	
	100		

G 55 Transparent

White lead	48	Temperature	C/05-03
Soda feldspar	18	Surface @ C/05	Gloss
Flint	15	Fluidity	None
Whiting	11	Stain penetration	Yes
Plastic kaolin	4	Opacity	Transparent
Calcined kaolin	4	Color / oxidation	Slight cream (6)
	——	Note: Some cracks	
	100		

G 56 Semigloss to Gloss

White lead	45	Temperature	C/05-04
Soda feldspar	20	Surface @ C/05	Semigloss
Flint	16	Fluidity	None
Whiting	12	Stain penetration	Yes
China clay	7	Opacity	Transparent
	——	Color / oxidation	Clear
	100	Note: Some cracks	

G 57 Leadless

Soda feldspar	39.40	Temperature	C/05
Flint	29.42	Surface @ C/05	Semigloss
Cryolite	11.48	Fluidity	None
Zinc oxide	8.69	Stain penetration	Yes
Soda ash	6.96	Opacity	Transparent
Whiting	4.05	Color / oxidation	Clear
	____	Note: Some cracks	
	100.00		

G 58 Semimat

Soda feldspar	35.55	Temperature	C/05-02
White lead	24.41	Surface @ C/05	Semimat
Colemanite	14.22	Fluidity	None
China clay	8.77	Stain penetration	Yes
Flint	6.16	Opacity	Transparent
Whiting	2.84	Color / oxidation	Clear, slight yellow
Barium carbonate	2.84		where thick
Rutile	2.84		
Zinc oxide	2.37		
	____		
	100.00		

G 59 Semigloss

White lead	25.47	Temperature	C/05
Colemanite	22.65	Surface @ C/05	Semigloss
Soda feldspar	17.92	Fluidity	Little
Flint	16.05	Stain penetration	Yes
China clay	4.72	Opacity	Transparent
Whiting	4.72	Color / oxidation	Clear, some white
Tin oxide	4.72		where thick
Plaster	3.77		
	____		
	100.02		

G 60 Cullet Semigloss

Cullet	50	Temperature	C/05-04
White lead	27	Surface @ C/05	Smooth semigloss
China clay	14	Fluidity	None
Tin oxide	9	Stain penetration	Darks show
	———	Opacity	Translucent, thin
	100		Opaque, thick
		Color / oxidation	White (32)

G 61 White Lead Opaque

White lead	47.5	Temperature	C/05
Soda feldspar	25.8	Surface @ C/05	Mat
Tin oxide	12.4	Fluidity	None
China clay	4.4	Stain penetration	Yes
Kentucky ball clay	4.1	Opacity	Translucent
Zinc oxide	3.6	Color / oxidation	White (32)
Flint	2.2		
	———		
	100.0		

G 62 Yellow-orange (J. W. Conrad, Mesa College, San Diego, California)

White lead	42.6	Temperature	C/05-02
Soda feldspar	18.5	Surface @ C/05	Mat
China clay	14.8	Fluidity	None
Whiting	10.2	Stain penetration	Yes
Flint	6.5	Opacity	Translucent, thin
Uranium oxide	5.6	Color / oxidation	Yellow-orange (18)
Yellow stain	1.8		
	———		
	100.0		

Note: Grind and mix completely

G 63 Light Pink

White lead	35	Temperature	C/05-04
Flint	20	Surface @ C/04	Semigloss
Soda feldspar	17	Fluidity	None
China clay	12	Stain penetration	Yes
Whiting	8	Opacity	Translucent
Pink stain	5	Color / oxidation	Light pink (45)
Tin oxide	3		

100

G 64 Blue Mat

Flint	53.0	Temperature	C/05-03
Lithium carbonate	26.0	Surface @ C/05	Mat
Kaolin	12.0	Fluidity	None
Copper carbonate	3.7	Stain penetration	Darks show
Soda ash	3.3	Opacity	Translucent
Bentonite	2.0	Color / oxidation	Lithium blue (84)

100.0

G 65 Blue-purple

Boric acid	60.0	Temperature	C/05
Flint	15.0	Surface @ C/05	Gloss
Soda ash	15.0	Fluidity	Little
Magnesium carbonate	7.0	Stain penetration	Darks show
Lithium carbonate	1.7	Opacity	Translucent
Cobalt oxide	1.3	Color / oxidation	Blue-purple

100.0

Note: Use over white clay

Medium-Temperature Glaze Formulas Cone/04-4

A glaze is a fused layer of glasslike materials on the surface of a clay body. The purpose of this layer is to give the surface color, protective finish, hardness, texture, and decoration. Glazes that mature when fired at the temperature range of 2014° to 2167°F. are known as medium-temperature glazes. The clay becomes harder and will not break or chip as easily as the low-temperature clays. The variety of colors produced is similar to those obtained with low-temperature glazes. This temperature firing range is popular with diverse groups of ceramists for the color range and cost. The kilns for firing low- and medium-temperature glazes and clays are much cheaper, due to the lower cost of kiln elements and insulation, than the kilns needed higher-temperature firing clays and glazes.

The following formulas are organized into four temperature groups; subdivided as to gloss, semigloss, and mat surfaces; distinguished as to transparent, translucent, and opaque qualities; and followed by color and special-effect glazes.

CONE/04

G 66 Lead Gloss

White lead	70	Temperature	C/04
Flint	8	Surface @ C/04	Gloss
Georgia clay	8	Fluidity	Very fluid
Soda feldspar	7	Stain penetration	Yes
Zinc oxide	6	Opacity	Transparent
Borax	1	Color / oxidation	Clear
	100		

G 67 Transparent

White lead	63	Temperature	C/04
Flint	30	Surface @ C/04	Gloss
China clay	7	Fluidity	Fluid
	____	Stain penetration	Yes
	100	Opacity	Transparent
		Color / oxidation	Clear
		Note: Crackle	

G 68 Volcanic Ash

Volcanic ash	59	Temperature	C/04
Colemanite	19	Surface @ C/04	Gloss, butter finish
White lead	10	Fluidity	Some
Borax	9	Stain penetration	Yes
Soda feldspar	3	Opacity	Transparent
	____	Color / oxidation	Clear
	100	Note: Crackle	

G 69 Gloss Finish

White lead	53	Temperature	C/04
Flint	27	Surface @ C/04	Gloss
Kentucky ball #4	12	Fluidity	Fluid
Whiting	5	Stain penetration	Yes
Zinc oxide	2	Opacity	Transparent
Tin oxide	1	Color / oxidation	Clear
	____	Note: Some cracks	
	100		

G 70 Transparent Gloss

White lead	51	Temperature	C/04
Kona spar	20	Surface @ C/04	High gloss
Flint	19	Fluidity	Fluid
Whiting	6	Stain penetration	Yes
China clay	4	Opacity	Transparent
	____	Color / oxidation	Clear
	100	Note: Some cracks	

G 71 Colemanite (Don Pilcher, Urbana, Illinois)

Colemanite	50.0	Temperature	C/04
Silica	25.0	Surface @ C/04	Gloss
Potash feldspar	12.5	Fluidity	None
Kaolin	12.5	Stain penetration	Yes
	———	Opacity	Transparent
	100.0	Color / oxidation	Clear
		Note: Some cracks	

G 72 Lead Gloss

White lead	46.00	Temperature	C/04
Flint	21.48	Surface @ C/04	Gloss
Potash feldspar	16.59	Fluidity	Some
China clay	7.69	Stain penetration	Yes
Whiting	5.94	Opacity	Transparent
Zinc oxide	2.30	Color / oxidation	Clear
	———	Note: Some cracks	
	100.00		

G 73 Clear Lead

White lead	45	Temperature	C/04
Kona feldspar	32	Surface @ C/04	Gloss
Flint	12	Fluidity	Fluid
Whiting	6	Stain penetration	Yes
China clay	3	Opacity	Transparent
Talc	2	Color / oxidation	Clear
	———	Note: Some cracks	
	100		

G 74 Transparent

White lead	44.5	Temperature	C/04-02
Flint	28.7	Surface @ C/04	Gloss
Potash feldspar	16.1	Fluidity	Some
Zinc oxide	4.6	Stain penetration	Yes
Calcined clay	3.1	Opacity	Transparent
Whiting	3.0	Color / oxidation	Clear
	___	Note: Some cracks	
	100.0		

G 75 Transparent Lead

White lead	40	Temperature	C/04
Soda feldspar	29	Surface @ C/04	Gloss
Flint	17	Fluidity	Slight
Cornwall stone	9	Stain penetration	Yes
Whiting	5	Opacity	Transparent
	___	Color / oxidation	Clear
	100	Note: Some cracks	

G 76 Transparent

White lead	41.59	Temperature	C/04
Flint	19.88	Surface @ C/04	Gloss
Soda feldspar	13.76	Fluidity	None
China clay	7.95	Stain penetration	Yes
Calcined clay	6.12	Opacity	Transparent
Zinc oxide	5.81	Color / oxidation	Clear
Whiting	4.89		
	___		
	100.00		

G 77 Transparent Leadless

Soda feldspar	41.35	Temperature	C/04
Colemanite	23.60	Surface @ C/04	Smooth gloss
Flint	19.22	Fluidity	Little
Zinc oxide	6.96	Stain penetration	Yes
Barium carbonate	5.64	Opacity	Transparent
Georgia clay	3.23	Color / oxidation	Clear
	——	Note: Some cracks	
	100.00		

G 78 Clear Colemanite

Colemanite	38	Temperature	C/04
Potash feldspar	37	Surface @ C/04	Smooth gloss
Barium carbonate	14	Fluidity	Some
Flint	11	Stain penetration	Yes
	——	Opacity	Transparent
	100	Color / oxidation	Clear
		Note: Crackle	

G 79 Kona Feldspar

Kona feldspar	30	Temperature	C/04
White lead	30	Surface @ C/04	Gloss
Flint	18	Fluidity	Little
Whiting	8	Stain penetration	Yes
China clay	7	Opacity	Transparent
Colemanite	6	Color / oxidation	Clear
Zinc oxide	1	Note: Some cracks	
	——		
	100		

G 80 Transparent

White lead	30	Temperature	C/04
Borax	23	Surface @ C/04	Smooth gloss
Potash feldspar	18	Fluidity	Some
Flint	18	Stain penetration	Yes
China clay	8	Opacity	Transparent
Whiting	3	Color / oxidation	Clear
	———	Note: Some cracks	
	100		

G 81 Opaque White

Frit #2106	78	Temperature	C/04
Zircopax	16	Surface @ C/04	Gloss
China clay	6	Fluidity	Fluid
	———	Stain penetration	Darks show
	100	Opacity	Translucent, thin
			Opaque, thick
		Color / oxidation	Milk white (32)

G 82 Gloss White

Red lead	38.3	Temperature	C/04
Flint	31.3	Surface @ C/04	Gloss
Borax	9.1	Fluidity	Fluid
Tin oxide	7.3	Stain penetration	Yes
China clay	4.5	Opacity	Transparent
Colemanite	4.5	Color / oxidation	Milk white (32)
Alumina oxide	4.1		
Soda ash	.9		
	———		
	100.0		

G 83 Translucent Gloss

White lead	55	Temperature	C/04
Flint	20	Surface @ C/04	Gloss
Kentucky ball #4	10	Fluidity	Some
Zircopax	10	Stain penetration	Yes
Borax	5	Opacity	Translucent
		Color / oxidation	Slight cream (6)
	100		

G 84 Milky White

Frit # 399	49	Temperature	C/04
Potash feldspar	19	Surface @ C/04	Gloss
Flint	16	Fluidity	Some
E.P. kaolin	6	Stain penetration	Some
Whiting	5	Opacity	Translucent
Zinc oxide	5	Color / oxidation	Milky white (32)
		Note: Some cracks	
	100		

G 85 Translucent Gloss

White lead	45.88	Temperature	C/04-02
Potash feldspar	18.94	Surface @ C/04	Gloss
Flint	10.97	Fluidity	Some
Whiting	8.89	Stain penetration	Yes
Tin oxide	8.89	Opacity	Translucent
Kaolin	6.43	Color / oxidation	Ivory (15)
	100.00		

G 86 Borax Gloss

Borax	32	Temperature	C/04
Flint	25	Surface @ C/04	Gloss
Soda feldspar	19	Fluidity	Fluid
Zinc oxide	10	Stain penetration	Yes
Whiting	9	Opacity	Translucent
Kaolin	5	Color / oxidation	Milky white (64) with slight blue tinge
	100	Note: Crackle	

G 87 Transparent Semigloss

Frit #28	65.75	Temperature	C/04
Soda feldspar	17.14	Surface @ C/04	Semigloss
Georgia clay	10.82	Fluidity	None
Nepheline syenite	6.29	Stain penetration	Yes
		Opacity	Transparent
	100.00	Color / oxidation	Slight cream (152)

G 88 Kona Feldspar Semigloss

White lead	45	Temperature	C/04
Kona feldspar	39	Surface @ C/04	Semigloss
China clay	6	Fluidity	None
Whiting	6	Stain penetration	Yes
Flint	3	Opacity	Transparent, thin
Tin oxide	1	Color / oxidation	Clear
	100		

G 89 Semigloss

White lead	44.35	Temperature	C/04
Potash feldspar	30.24	Surface @ C/04	Semigloss
Flint	11.50	Fluidity	Some
Whiting	5.80	Stain penetration	Yes
Barium carbonate	3.48	Opacity	Transparent
China clay	2.90	Color / oxidation	Clear
Talc	1.73	Note: Some cracks	
	100.00		

G 90 Lead Semigloss

White lead	40	Temperature	C/04
Kona feldspar	20	Surface @ C/04	Semigloss
Flint	15	Fluidity	None
Barium carbonate	15	Stain penetration	Yes
Whiting	5	Opacity	Translucent, thick
China clay	3	Color / oxidation	Slight white
Lithium carbonate	2		
	100		

G 91 Clear Semigloss

Potash feldspar	37	Temperature	C/04
Colemanite	21	Surface @ C/04	Semigloss
Barium carbonate	21	Fluidity	None
Flint	17	Stain penetration	Yes
Kaolin	4	Opacity	Transparent
		Color / oxidation	Clear
	100	Note: Some cracks	

G 92 Lithium Semigloss

Flint	36.9	Temperature	C/04
Lithium carbonate	18.5	Surface @ C/04	Semigloss
White lead	16.4	Fluidity	Very fluid
Kaolin	11.6	Stain penetration	Yes
Bone ash	8.2	Opacity	Clear, thin
Soda feldspar	6.1		Opaque, thick
Bentonite	2.3	Color / oxidation	Milky where thick
	100.0		

G 93 Clear Semigloss

Flint	27.07	Temperature	C/04
Soda feldspar	26.40	Surface @ C/04	Semigloss
Borax	22.67	Fluidity	Some
White lead	18.38	Stain penetration	Yes
Whiting	3.56	Opacity	Transparent
Zinc oxide	1.92	Color / oxidation	Clear
		Note: Some cracks	
	100.00		

G 94 Translucent

White lead	41.76	Temperature	C/04
Borax	25.08	Surface @ C/04	Semigloss
Tin oxide	15.76	Fluidity	Little
Flint	14.45	Stain penetration	Darks show
Zinc oxide	1.77	Opacity	Translucent
Soda ash	1.88	Color / oxidation	Light cream (31)
		Note: Broken white areas	
	100.70		

G 95 Translucent Semigloss

Volcanic ash	33.71	Temperature	C/04
Colemanite	22.47	Surface @ C/04	Semigloss
Kaolin	19.66	Fluidity	None
White lead	6.74	Stain penetration	Yes
Tin oxide	6.74	Opacity	Translucent
Borax	4.49	Color / oxidation	Slight tan (30)
Zinc oxide	3.32	Note: Some tan specks	
Barium carbonate	2.82		

99.95

G 96 Translucent-opaque

Flint	30.25	Temperature	C/04-02
Borax	25.55	Surface @ C/04	Semigloss
White lead	13.45	Fluidity	Little
Potash feldspar	9.08	Stain penetration	Darks show
Tin oxide	7.56	Opacity	Translucent, thin
Soda ash	6.72		Opaque, thick
Calcined clay	4.03	Color / oxidation	White (48)
Kaolin	3.36		

100.00

G 97 Semimat

Flint	23.98	Temperature	C/04-02
Soda ash	21.10	Surface @ C/04	Semimat
Calcined borax	17.27	Fluidity	None
Soda feldspar	13.91	Stain penetration	Yes
Whiting	9.11	Opacity	Transparent
White lead	8.63	Color / oxidation	Slight white / White
Kaolin	6.00		(64)

100.00

G 98 White Translucent

Kona feldspar	41	Temperature	C/04
White lead	39	Surface @ C/04	Semimat
Whiting	8	Fluidity	None
Flint	5	Stain penetration	Yes
China clay	5	Opacity	Translucent
Magnesium carbonate	2	Color / oxidation	White (63)

100

G 99 Cream White

White lead	38.10	Temperature	C/04
Potash feldspar	28.57	Surface @ C/04	Semimat, smooth
Kaolin	14.29	Fluidity	None
Whiting	9.52	Stain penetration	Yes
Flint	4.76	Opacity	Translucent
Zinc oxide	4.76	Color / oxidation	Cream (64)

100.00

G 100 Semimat Translucent

Flint	37.17	Temperature	C/04
Lithium carbonate	18.55	Surface @ C/04	Semimat
White lead	17.24	Fluidity	Some
Kaolin	10.76	Stain penetration	Yes
Bone ash	8.28	Opacity	Translucent
Soda feldspar	6.21	Color / oxidation	White (63)
Bentonite	1.79	Note: Crackle	

100.00

G 101 Translucent-opaque

White lead	35.24	Temperature	C/04-02
Soda feldspar	18.65	Surface @ C/04	Semimat
Kaolin	17.10	Fluidity	Little
Whiting	9.89	Stain penetration	Darks show
Tin oxide	8.25	Opacity	Translucent, thin
Flint	7.70		Opaque, thick
Zinc oxide	3.17	Color / oxidation	Off-white (64)
	100.00		

G 102 Cream Mat

White lead	54.62	Temperature	C/04
Flint	16.81	Surface @ C/04	Smooth mat
Soda feldspar	10.08	Fluidity	Fluid
Tin oxide	8.40	Stain penetration	Darks show
Rutile	5.88	Opacity	Translucent, thin
China clay	2.52		Opaque, thick
Borax	1.69	Color / oxidation	Cream (15)
	100.00		

G 103 Translucent Mat (W. Mills, Carnegie-Mellon University, Pittsburgh, Pennsylvania)

White lead	51.86	Temperature	C/04-2
Calcined clay	10.05	Surface @ C/04	Smooth mat
Soda feldspar	9.89	Fluidity	None
Nepheline syenite	8.10	Stain penetration	Yes
Barium carbonate	6.32	Opacity	Translucent
Whiting	5.67	Color / oxidation	Slight cream (29)
Flint	4.86	Note: Mix well	
Tin oxide	3.25		
	100.00		

G 104 Translucent Mat, White

Kona feldspar	46	Temperature	C/04
Whiting	13	Surface @ C/04	Mat
Barium carbonate	13	Fluidity	None
Colemanite	12	Stain penetration	Yes
Flint	10	Opacity	Translucent
Zinc oxide	3	Color / oxidation	White (6)
Tin oxide	3		
	100		

G 105 Lead Mat

White lead	46	Temperature	C/04
Soda feldspar	20	Surface @ C/04	Mat
Kaolin	16	Fluidity	Little
Whiting	11	Stain penetration	Yes
Flint	7	Opacity	Translucent
		Color / oxidation	Slight yellow (5)
	100		

G 106 Cream Mat

White lead	43	Temperature	C/04-02
Kona feldspar	39	Surface @ C/02	Smooth mat
Barium carbonate	11	Fluidity	None
Flint	4	Stain penetration	Yes
China clay	2	Opacity	Translucent
Zinc oxide	1	Color / oxidation	Cream (6)
	100		

G 107 Soft Satin Mat

White lead	42.16	Temperature	C/04-02
Kentucky ball #4	21.18	Surface @ C/04	Mat
Soda feldspar	17.71	Fluidity	None
Whiting	10.40	Stain penetration	Yes
Flint	8.55	Opacity	Translucent
		Color / oxidation	Cream (5)
	100.00		

G 108 Translucent Mat

White lead	42	Temperature	C/04-02
Potash feldspar	20	Surface @ C/04	Mat
Barium carbonate	12	Fluidity	Some
Flint	12	Stain penetration	Yes
Calcined kaolin	7	Opacity	Translucent
Whiting	6	Color / oxidation	Cream (6)
Zinc oxide	1		
	100		

G 109 Mat

White lead	40.91	Temperature	C/04
Soda feldspar	27.27	Surface @ C/04	Mat
Georgia clay	13.64	Fluidity	Some
Whiting	9.09	Stain penetration	Darks show
Flint	4.54	Opacity	Translucent
Zinc oxide	2.72	Color / oxidation	Cream (6)
Bentonite	1.83		
	100.00		

G 110 Lead Mat

White lead	40.7	Temperature	C/04
Soda feldspar	25.9	Surface @ C/04	Mat
China clay	18.5	Fluidity	None
Whiting	6.3	Stain penetration	Yes
Flint	5.5	Opacity	Translucent
Zinc oxide	3.1	Color / oxidation	Cream (6)

100.0

G 111 Cream Mat

White lead	40	Temperature	C/04-02
Potash feldspar	22	Surface @ C/04	Mat
Barium carbonate	11	Fluidity	None
Kaolin	11	Stain penetration	Yes
Flint	8	Opacity	Translucent
Whiting	7	Color / oxidation	Cream (6)
Tin oxide	1		

100

G 112 Mat

White lead	49.55	Temperature	C/04-02
Potash feldspar	21.71	Surface @ C/04	Dry mat
Calcined kaolin	12.68	Fluidity	None
Whiting	11.97	Stain penetration	Yes
Kaolin	4.09	Opacity	Translucent
		Color / oxidation	Slight yellow-cream (15)

100.00

G 113 Wood Ash

White lead	45.7	Temperature	C/04-02
Soda feldspar	27.6	Surface @ C/04	Dry mat
Wood ash, mixed	13.2	Fluidity	None
Ball clay	12.1	Stain penetration	Yes
Calcined clay	1.4	Opacity	Translucent
	———	Color / oxidation	Slightly grayed purple
	100.0		(109)

Note: Color depends upon the ash used

G 114 Bright Yellow

White lead	56.40	Temperature	C/04
Soda feldspar	31.93	Surface @ C/04	Bright gloss
Flint	4.40	Fluidity	Some
Kaolin	3.66	Stain penetration	Darks show
Antimony oxide	3.61	Opacity	Opaque
	———	Color / oxidation	Bright medium yellow
	100.00		(12)

G 115 Yellow

Frit #14	48.94	Temperature	C/04
Uranium oxide	25.53	Surface @ C/04	Gloss
Soda feldspar	12.77	Fluidity	Fluid
Kaolin	8.08	Stain penetration	Yes
Nepheline syenite	4.68	Opacity	Transparent
	———	Color / oxidation	Yellow (3)
	100.00		

Note: Use over white engobe, grind and mix thoroughly

G 116 Tan

White lead	62.58	Temperature	C/04
Soda feldspar	13.78	Surface @ C/04	Gloss
Flint	10.59	Fluidity	Some
Tin oxide	7.66	Stain penetration	Yes
Barium carbonate	3.26	Opacity	Transparent
Georgia clay	2.13	Color / oxidation	Tan (28)
Nickel oxide, green	.33		
	100.33		

G 117 Semigloss Rutile

White lead	62	Temperature	C/04
Kaolin	14	Surface @ C/04	Semigloss
Flint	13	Fluidity	Some
Rutile	6	Stain penetration	Darks show
Plastic vitrox clay	4	Opacity	Translucent
Zinc oxide	1	Color / oxidation	Rust-orange, with broken orange-tan (22)
	100		

G 118 Semimat Broken Tan

White lead	61.2	Temperature	C/04
Potash feldspar	18.3	Surface @ C/04	Mat
Borax	11.6	Fluidity	Some
Rutile	4.6	Stain penetration	Darks show
Calcined kaolin	2.8	Opacity	Translucent
Kaolin	1.0	Color / oxidation	Broken warm tan, orange spotting (23)
Zinc oxide	.5		
	100.0		

G 119 Transparent Amber

Red lead	50	Temperature	C/04
Flint	25	Surface @ C/04	Gloss
Red clay	25	Fluidity	Fluid
	———	Stain penetration	Yes
	100	Opacity	Transparent
		Color / oxidation	Amber (19)
		Note: Some cracks	

G 120 Semigloss Rutile

White lead	54.96	Temperature	C/04
Flint	18.71	Surface @ C/04	Semigloss
Rutile	12.29	Fluidity	None
Soda feldspar	10.58	Stain penetration	Yes
China clay	3.46	Opacity	Translucent
	———	Color / oxidation	Warm medium ochre
	100.00		(10)

G 121 Orange green

White lead	70.06	Temperature	C/04
Flint	13.46	Surface @ C/04	Gloss
China clay	7.23	Fluidity	Very fluid
Potassium bichromate	5.05	Stain penetration	Darks show
Tin oxide	4.20	Opacity	Translucent
	———	Color / oxidation	Broken dark orange
	100.00		and dark green

G 122 Artificial Reduction Red

Frit #170	35.58	Temperature	C/04
Flint	26.69	Surface @ C/04	Gloss
White lead	21.75	Fluidity	Fluid
Kaolin	9.88	Stain penetration	No
Zinc oxide	2.97	Opacity	Opaque
Whiting	1.98	Color / oxidation	Deep red, spotty
Copper carbonate	.66		purple, greens, black
Silicon carbide	.49		
	100.00		

G 123 Turquoise Blue

Colemanite	28.1	Temperature	C/04
Flint	25.5	Surface @ C/04	Gloss
Soda feldspar	19.8	Fluidity	None
White lead	8.7	Stain penetration	Darks show
Tin oxide	6.6	Opacity	Translucent, thin
Copper oxide	3.3		Opaque, thick
Kaolin	3.0	Color / oxidation	Turquoise (84)
Barium carbonate	3.0		
Zinc oxide	1.1		
Lithium carbonate	.9		
	100.0		

G 124 Semigloss Turquoise

Potash feldspar	24.2	Temperature	C/04
Borax	23.3	Surface @ C/04	Semigloss
White lead	17.5	Fluidity	None
Flint	11.5	Stain penetration	Darks show
Whiting	11.3	Opacity	Translucent
Tin oxide	8.2	Color / oxidation	Medium turquoise
Copper carbonate	3.5		(84)
Lithium carbonate	.7		
	100.2		

G 125 Reduction Celadon

Soda feldspar	49.0	Temperature	C/04
Soda ash	25.0	Surface @ C/04	Semigloss
White lead	19.6	Fluidity	None
Whiting	2.4	Stain penetration	Yes
Tin oxide	2.3	Opacity	Translucent
Red iron oxide	1.7	Color / oxidation	Slight gray (light 143)
	———	/ reduction	Slight green-gray
	100.0		(light 141)

Note: Use over clay containing iron

G 126 Chartreuse Mat (Don Pilcher, Urbana, Illinois)

White lead	40.9	Temperature	C/04
Barium carbonate	25.6	Surface @ C/04	Semigloss
Silica	20.2	Fluidity	Little
Kaolin	11.3	Stain penetration	Darks show
Chromium oxide	2.0	Opacity	Translucent
	———	Color / oxidation	Bright chartreuse
	100.0		(144)

Note: Grind and mix thoroughly use over white clay

G 127 Chrome Green

Flint	40.0	Temperature	C/04
Borax	38.0	Surface @ C/04	Semigloss
Chromium oxide, green	12.0	Fluidity	None
Boric acid	3.0	Stain penetration	None
Kaolin	2.4	Opacity	Opaque
Colemanite	1.6	Color / oxidation	Dark chrome-green
	———		(dark 122)
	97.0		

G 128 Dark Green, Orange Spot

White lead	68.00	Temperature	C/04
Flint	13.64	Surface @ C/04	Gloss
China clay	8.61	Fluidity	Very fluid
Potassium bichromate	4.95	Stain penetration	Darks show
Tin oxide	4.80	Opacity	Translucent
	———	Color / oxidation	Dark green, orange
	100.00	in recessed areas and bottom of	
		bowls (dark 141)	

G 129 Green

White lead	32.1	Temperature	C/04
Soda feldspar	23.0	Surface @ C/04	Gloss
Flint	17.0	Fluidity	Little
Soda ash	17.0	Stain penetration	Darks show
Copper carbonate	3.9	Opacity	Translucent, thin
Tin oxide	2.9		Opaque, thick
Zinc oxide	2.8	Color / oxidation	Green (139)
Chromium oxide	.3	Note For bright green use 7.8 tin oxide	
	———		
	99.0		

G 130 Goldstone

White lead	58.0	Temperature	C/04
Soda feldspar	24.3	Surface @ C/04	High gloss
Flint	12.1	Fluidity .	Some
Red iron oxide	3.3	Stain penetration	None
Whiting	2.3	Opacity	Opaque
	———	Color / oxidation Dark brown with gold	
	100.0	specks, red-brown where thick (74)	
		Note: Mix thin wash of potassium	
		dichrome and water, put on clay,	
		glaze over	

G 131 Aventurine "Gold-Spangled Brown"

Borax	57.28	Temperature	C/04
Flint	25.02	Surface @ C/04	Semigloss
Red iron oxide	14.14	Fluidity	Some
Boric acid	3.50	Stain penetration	None
Cobalt carbonate	.04	Opacity	Opaque
Copper carbonate	.02	Color / oxidation	Dark brown with gold specks (dark 50)
	100.00		

G 132 Amber-brown (J. W. Conrad, Mesa College, San Diego, California)

White lead	48.7	Temperature	C/04
Potash feldspar	19.0	Surface @ C/04	High gloss
Flint	17.5	Fluidity	Fluid
Red iron oxide	6.6	Stain penetration	Yes
Whiting	5.4	Opacity	Transparent
China clay	2.8	Color / oxidation	Rich amber-brown (34)
	100.0		

G 133 Aventurine

Borax	45	Temperature	C/04
Soda feldspar	22	Surface @ C/04	Gloss
Flint	20	Fluidity	Fluid
White lead	10		
Kaolin	3		
	100		
Copper red oxide	4	Stain penetration	Darks show
		Opacity	Translucent
		Color / oxidation	Dark green, some gold specks (97)
Uranium oxide	3.5	Stain penetration	Yes
		Opacity	Translucent
		Color / oxidation	Slight yellow, occasional gold specks (14)

G 134 Satin Black

Litharge	75.2	Temperature	C/04
Cornwall stone	11.3	Surface @ C/04	Satin
Manganese dioxide	7.5	Fluidity	Some
Red clay	4.5	Stain penetration	None
Red iron oxide	1.5	Opacity	Opaque
	———	Color / oxidation	Black (145)
	100.0		

G 135 Mirror Black

White lead	48.0	Temperature	C/04
Flint	26.4	Surface @ C/04	High gloss
Kaolin	8.7	Fluidity	Little
Whiting	5.3	Stain penetration	None
Soda ash	5.0	Opacity	Opaque
Cobalt oxide	2.6	Color / oxidation	Black (113)
Red iron oxide	2.0		
Manganese dioxide	2.0		
	———		
	100.0		

G 136 Black and White (J. W. Conrad, Mesa College, San Diego, California)

(apply under)

White lead	59.0	Temperature	C/04
Bernard clay	41.0	Surface @ C/04	Mat
	———	Fluidity	Little
	100.0	Stain penetration	None
(apply over)		Opacity	Opaque
White lead	52.4	Color / oxidation	White with broken
Soda feldspar	31.8		areas of black (145)
Kaolin	4.9		
Ball clay	4.5		
Zinc oxide	4.0		
Flint	2.4		
	———		
	100.0		

CONE/03-02

G 137 Transparent Gloss

Red lead	60	Temperature	C/03-02
Silica	23	Surface @ C/02	Gloss
China clay	15	Fluidity	Very fluid
Soda feldspar	2	Stain penetration	Yes
		Opacity	Transparent
	100	Color / oxidation	Clear

G 138 Transparent

White lead	53.39	Temperature	C/02-2
Soda feldspar	22.71	Surface @ C/02	Gloss
Flint	12.69	Fluidity	Some
Kaolin	5.90	Stain penetration	Yes
Whiting	5.31	Opacity	Transparent
		Color / oxidation	Clear
	100.00	Note: Some cracks	

G 139 White Gloss

Red lead	62.2	Temperature	C/02-01
Flint	15.5	Surface @ C/02	Smooth gloss
Tin oxide	10.0	Fluidity	Some
China clay, calcined	8.3	Stain penetration	Yes
China clay	4.0	Opacity	Translucent
		Color / oxidation	Cream-white (136)
	100.0		

G 140 Opaque White

Soda feldspar	34	Temperature	C/02
White lead	33	Surface @ C/02	Gloss
Tin oxide	10	Fluidity	None
Flint	8	Stain penetration	Darks show
Whiting	8	Opacity	Translucent, thin
Zinc oxide	4		Opaque, thick
Kaolin	3	Color / oxidation	White (48)
	100		

G 141 Semigloss Crackle

White lead	23.44	Temperature	C/02-1
Zircopax	21.79	Surface @ C/02	Semigloss
Borax	18.86	Fluidity	Little
Flint	14.47	Satin penetration	Darks show
Potash feldspar	10.26	Opacity	Opaque
Calcined kaolin	5.13	Color / oxidation	White (32)
Kaolin	3.30	Note: Some cracks	
Whiting	2.75		
	100.00		

G 142 Mat White

White lead	44	Temperature	C/02
Soda feldspar	35	Surface @ C/02	Mat
Whiting	10	Fluidity	None
Calcined kaolin	7	Stain penetration	Yes
Kaolin	4	Opacity	Translucent
		Color / oxidation	Cool white (5)
	100		

G 143 Dry Mat

White lead	49	Temperature	C/03-01
Potash feldspar	24	Surface @ C/02	Dry mat
Calcined clay	12	Fluidity	None
Whiting	11	Stain penetration	Yes
Kaolin	4	Opacity	Translucent
		Color / oxidation	Blue-grayed white
	100		(16)

G 144 Yellow Transparent

Red lead	60.0	Temperature	C/03-02
Flint	23.0	Surface @ C/02	Gloss
China clay	12.0	Fluidity	Fluid
Red iron oxide	2.6	Stain penetration	Yes
Potash feldspar	2.4	Opacity	Transparent
		Color / oxidation	Slight yellow (6)
	100.0		

G 145 Rutile Tan

White lead	65	Temperature	C/03-02
Flint	14	Surface @ C/02	Gloss and mat
Potash feldspar	10	Fluidity	Fluid
Rutile	7	Stain penetration	Darks show
Kaolin	2	Opacity	Translucent and opaque
Zinc oxide	2	Color / oxidation	Broken tan, yellow, and brown (13)
	100		

G 146 Yellow-green

Red lead	63.4	Temperature	C/02-2
Flint	16.3	Surface @ C/02	Gloss
Calcined kaolin	8.6	Fluidity	Some
China clay	5.2	Stain penetration	Darks show
Copper oxide	2.7	Opacity	Translucent
Tin oxide	2.3	Color / oxidation	Yellow-green (125)
Iron oxide	.5	Note; Metallic over dark englobe or clay	
	99.0		

G 147 Metallic Black

Red lead	59.0	Temperature	C/03-02
Flint	22.0	Surface @ C/02	High gloss
China clay	11.6	Fluidity	Fluid
Cobalt oxide	2.1	Stain penetration	None
Soda feldspar	1.8	Opacity	Opaque
Copper oxide	1.3	Color / oxidation	Mirror blue-black
Manganese dioxide	1.3		(113)
Red iron oxide	.9	Note: Amost a metallic surface

100.0

G 148 Gloss Black

White lead	60	Temperature	C/02
Flint	18	Surface @ C/02	Smooth gloss
Manganese dioxide	10	Fluidity	Very fluid
Cornwall stone	6	Stain penetration	None
Red clay	6	Opacity	Opaque
		Color / oxidation	Dark brown-black
	100		(113)

CONE/1-2

G 149 Transparent Gloss

White lead	56	Temperature	C/1-2
Cornwall stone	15	Surface @ C/1	Smooth gloss
Flint	14	Fluidity	Little
Whiting	8	Stain penetration	Yes
Kentucky ball #4	7	Opacity	Transparent
	100	Color / oxidation	Clear

G 150 Clear Smooth Gloss

White lead	52	Temperature	C/1-2
Soda feldspar	16	Surface @ C/1	Smooth gloss
Cornwall stone	15	Fluidity	Some
Flint	10	Stain penetration	Yes
Whiting	4	Opacity	Transparent
Zinc oxide	3	Color / oxidation	Clear
	100		

G 151 Transparent

White lead	48.29	Temperature	C/2-4
Potash feldspar	27.88	Surface @ C/2	Gloss and semigloss
Whiting	16.51	Fluidity	Fluid
P.V. fire clay	7.32	Stain penetration	Yes
		Opacity	Transparent
	100.00	Color / oxidation	Slight yellow (13)
		Note: Some cracks	

G 152 Frit #3124

Frit #3124	47.28	Temperature	C/2-6
Flint	22.49	Surface @ C/2	Gloss
Soda feldspar	15.31	Fluidity	Little
Whiting	5.74	Stain penetration	Yes
Talc	4.78	Opacity	Transparent
Kaolin	3.83	Color / oxidation	Clear
	99.43		

G 153 Colemanite (Alfred University, Alfred, New York)

Potash feldspar	42.2	Temperature	C/2-6
Colemanite	24.1	Surface @ C/2	Gloss
Flint	18.5	Fluidity	Little
Zinc	9.4	Stain penetration	Yes
Kaolin	4.8	Opacity	Bright transparent
		Color / oxidation	Clear, blue-milky
	99.0		where thick

G 154 Bright Gloss

White lead	41	Temperature	C/1-2
Soda feldspar	29	Surface @ C/2	Smooth gloss
Flint	13	Fluidity	Some
Whiting	9	Stain penetration	Yes
Kaolin	5	Opacity	Transparent
Zinc oxide	4	Color / oxidation	Clear
	101		

G 155 Potash Feldspar Gloss

Potash feldspar	38.6	Temperature	C/2
Flint	22.5	Surface @ C/2	Gloss
Colemanite	17.6	Fluidity	Little
Zinc oxide	8.1	Stain penetration	Yes
Barium carbonate	6.8	Opacity	Transparent
Talc	6.4	Color / oxidation	Clear, blue-white where thick
	100.0		

G 156 Colemanite (Alfred University, Alfred, New York)

Potash feldspar	34.87	Temperature	C/2-6
Colemanite	31.45	Surface @ C/2	Gloss
Flint	19.82	Fluidity	Little
Kaolin	5.92	Stain penetration	Yes
Zinc oxide	4.89	Opacity	Transparent
Whiting	3.05	Color / oxidation	Clear, whitish where thick
	100.00		

G 157 Cornwall Stone

Cornwall stone	65	Temperature	C/2-4
White lead	21	Surface @ C/2	Gloss
Whiting	10	Fluidity	Little
Zinc oxide	2	Stain penetration	Yes
Tin oxide	2	Opacity	Slight translucent
		Color / oxidation	Whitish
	100		

G 158 Semigloss

Soda feldspar	43	Temperature	C/1-4
Flint	23	Surface @ C/2	Semigloss
Kentucky ball #4	10	Fluidity	None
Barium carbonate	8	Stain penetration	Yes
Zinc oxide	7	Opacity	Transparent
Whiting	7	Color / oxidation	Clear
Talc	2		
	100		

G 159 Semigloss Clear

P.V. clay	39	Temperature	C/2-4
White lead	29	Surface @ C/2	Semigloss
Potash feldspar	16	Fluidity	Little
Whiting	13	Stain penetration	Yes
Kaolin	3	Opacity	Transparent
		Color / oxidation	Clear
	100		

G 160 Semigloss Transparent

Potash feldspar	32	Temperature	C/2-6
Red lead	25	Surface @ C/2	Semigloss
Flint	20	Fluidity	Little
Whiting	9	Stain penetration	Yes
Kentucky ball #4	6	Opacity	Transparent
Kaolin	6	Color / oxidation	Clear
Zinc oxide	2		
	100		

G 161 Ivory Semigloss

Red lead	38	Temperature	C/1-2
Flint	22	Surface @ C/2	Semigloss
China clay	12	Fluidity	Some
Zinc oxide	8	Stain penetration	Darks show
Soda feldspar	5	Opacity	Opaque
Dolomite	5	Color / oxidation	Ivory (15)
Tin oxide	5		
Rutile	4		
	99		

G 162 Lead Semigloss

White lead	43.8	Temperature	C/1-2
Potash feldspar	27.9	Surface @ C/2	Semigloss
Whiting	11.7	Fluidity	Some
Kaolin	16.6	Stain penetration	Dark show
		Opacity	Translucent
	100.0	Color / oxidation	Slight yellow (3)

G 163 Mat

Potash feldspar	50	Temperature	C/2-4
Soda ash	28	Surface @ C/2	Mat
Flint	12	Fluidity	Some
Whiting	10	Stain penetration	Yes
		Opacity	Translucent
	100	Color / oxidation	Whitish (30)
		Note: Some cracks	

G 164 Ivory

Red lead	47.2	Temperature	C/1-2
China clay	29.0	Surface @ C/2	Mat
Flint	11.8	Fluidity	Some
Soda feldspar	6.6	Stain penetration	Yes
Dolomite	6.0	Opacity	Slight translucent
	———	Color / oxidation	Ivory (4)
	100.6		

G 165 Mat (J. W. Conrad, Mesa College, San Diego, California)

White lead	34.9	Temperature	C/2
Soda feldspar	33.2	Surface @ C/2	Smooth dry mat
China clay	15.5	Fluidity	None
Whiting	15.5	Stain penetration	Darks show
Zinc oxide	.9	Opacity	Translucent
	———	Color / oxidation	Off-white (16)
	100.0		

G 166 Orange

Red lead	59.6	Temperature	C/2-4
Uranium oxide	24.9	Surface @ C/2	Gloss and semigloss
Flint	15.0	Fluidity	Fluid
Tin oxide	1.5	Stain penetration	Darks show
	———	Opacity	Translucent
	101.0	Color / oxidation	Orange (70)
		Note: Grind	

G 167 Orange-red

Red lead	63	Temperature	C/2-4
Uranium oxide	17	Surface @ C/2	Semigloss
China clay	14	Fluidity	Fluid
Flint	4	Stain penetration	Darks show
Zinc oxide	2	Opacity	Translucent
	———	Color / oxidation	Orange-red (72)
	100	Note: Grind	

G 168 Dark Red

Red lead	38	Temperature	C/2-3
Flint	25	Surface @ C/2	Gloss
China clay	14	Fluidity	Some
Red stain	12	Stain penetration	Yes
Whiting	11	Opacity	Transparent
	———	Color / oxidation	Dark red (59)
	100	Note: Color depends upon stain used	

G 169 Reduction Red

Soda feldspar	33.0	Temperature	C/2
Borax	29.0	Surface @ C/2	Gloss
Flint	17.0	Fluidity	Little
Kaolin	12.0	Stain penetration	None
Fluorspar	6.0	Opacity	Opaque
Tin oxide	2.0	Color / oxidation	Blood red in areas,
Carborundum	.5		black areas
Copper carbonate	.5		
	———		
	100.0		

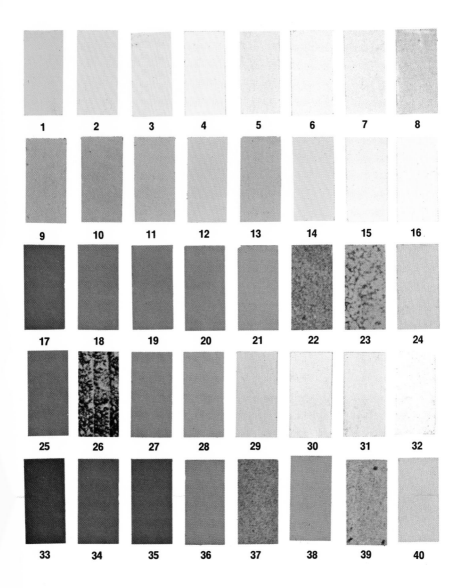

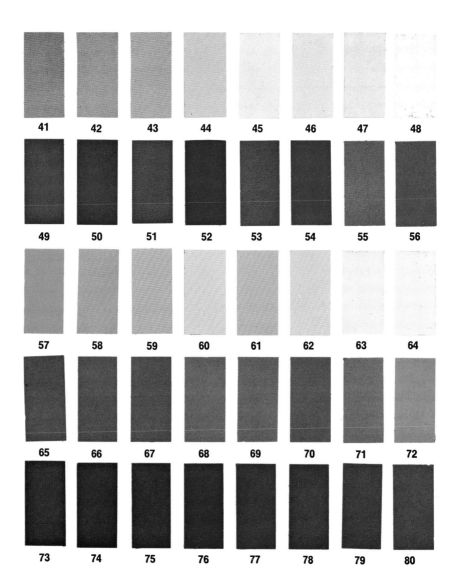

41 42 43 44 45 46 47 48

49 50 51 52 53 54 55 56

57 58 59 60 61 62 63 64

65 66 67 68 69 70 71 72

73 74 75 76 77 78 79 80

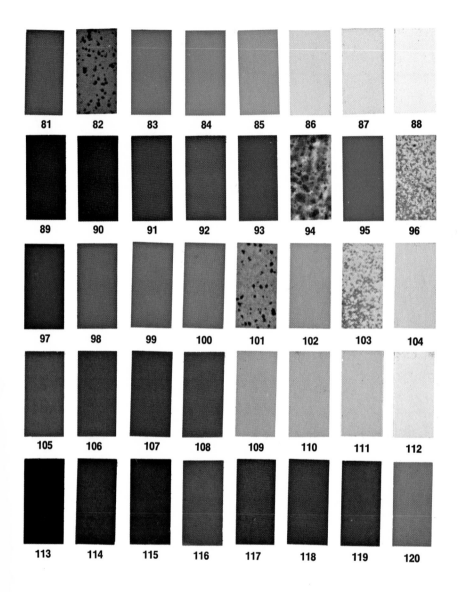

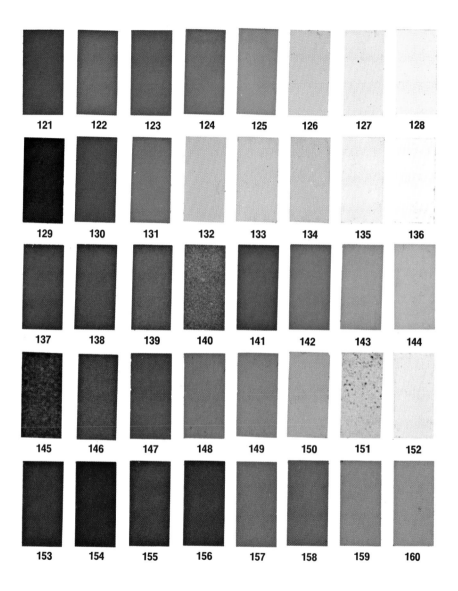

CONE/3

G 170 Gloss (J. W. Conrad, Mesa College, San Diego, California)

Frit # 24	52.5	Temperature	C/3-5
Kaolin	23.7	Surface @ C/4	Gloss
Zinc oxide	10.6	Fluidity	Fluid
Cornwall stone	7.8	Stain penetration	Yes
Whiting	5.4	Opacity	Transparent
	———	Color / oxidation	Clear
	100.0		

C 171 Clear Gloss

Buckingham feldspar	38.2	Temperature	C/3-4
Flint	22.3	Surface @ C/4	Gloss
Colemanite	17.4	Fluidity	Little
Zinc oxide	8.2	Stain penetration	Yes
Barium carbonate	· 6.6	Opacity	Transparent
Talc	6.4	Color / oxidation	Clear
Whiting	.9		
	———		
	100.0		

G 172 Semigloss

Potash feldspar	64	Temperature	C/3-7
Zinc oxide	15	Surface @ C/4	Semigloss
China clay	10	Fluidity	None
Whiting	9	Stain penetration	Yes
Flint	2	Opacity	Translucent
	———	Color / oxidation	Whitish
	100		

G 173 Semigloss

Potash feldspar	58	Temperature	C/3-7
Flint	19	Surface @ C/4	Semigloss
China clay	7	Fluidity	None
Zinc oxide	6	Stain penetration	Yes
Whiting	5	Opacity	Transparent
Barium carbonate	5	Color / oxidation	Clear
	100		

G 174 White Semigloss

Potash feldspar	43	Temperature	C/3-7
Flint	29	Surface @ C/4	Semigloss
China clay	12	Fluidity	None
Whiting	6	Stain penetration	Yes
Barium carbonate	6	Opacity	Translucent
Magnesium carbonate	2		Opaque, thick
Zinc oxide	2	Color / oxidation	Whitish (7)
	100		

G 175 Egg White Semigloss

Potash feldspar	40	Temperature	C/3-7
Flint	19	Surface @ C/4	Semigloss
China clay	15	Fluidity	None
Whiting	11	Stain penetration	Darks show
Barium carbonate	9	Opacity	Opaque
Zinc oxide	5	Color / oxidation	Egg white (6)
Magnesium carbonate	1	Note: Apply medium	
	100		

G 176 Semimat Clear

Potash feldspar	58	Temperature	C/3-7
Flint	12	Surface @ C/4	Smooth semimat
Whiting	12	Fluidity	Little
China clay	10	Stain penetration	Yes
Zinc oxide	6	Opacity	Transparent
	——	Color / oxidation	Clear
	98		

G 177 Dry Mat

Potash feldspar	52	Temperature	C/3-7
Whiting	19	Surface @ C/4	Dry mat
China clay	14	Fluidity	None
Zinc oxide	9	Stain penetration	Darks show
Flint	6	Opacity	Translucent
	——	Color / oxidation	White
	100		

G 178 Tan Semimat

Flint	40.0	Temperature	C/3-4
Zinc oxide	21.0	Surface @ C/4	Semimat
Boric acid	14.3	Fluidity	None
Soda ash	12.4	Stain penetration	Yes
Rutile	6.7	Opacity	Translucent
Kentucky ball #4	5.6	Color / oxidation	Tan, minute crystals on the surface (29)
	———		
	100.0		

G 179 Frit Aventurine (J. W. Conrad, Mesa College, San Diego, California)

Frit #24	71	Temperature	C/3
Red iron oxide	16	Surface @ C/3	Gloss
Whiting	8	Fluidity	Little
Kaolin	5	Stain penetration	None
	——	Opacity	Opaque
	100	Color / oxidation	Purple-brown-black, with gold specks where thick

CONE/4

G 180 Transparent Gloss

Volcanic ash	60	Temperature	C/4
Borax	28	Surface @ C/4	Gloss
Whiting	7	Fluidity	Some
Bentonite	5	Stain penetration	Yes
	———	Opacity	Transparent
	100	Color / oxidation	Clear

Note: Some cracks where thick

G 181 Gloss (J. W. Conrad, Mesa College, San Diego, California)

Kona feldspar	59.62	Temperature	C/4-6
E.P. kaolin	13.81	Surface @ C/4	Gloss
Flint	12.04	Fluidity	Little
Whiting	8.00	Stain penetration	Yes
Zinc oxide	6.53	Opacity	Transparent
	———	Color / oxidation	Clear
	100.00		

G 182 Gloss Kona Feldspar

Kona feldspar	47.4	Temperature	C/4-5
Colemanite	22.3	Surface @ C/4	Gloss
Flint	11.6	Fluidity	Some
Barium carbonate	8.0	Stain penetration	Yes
Kaolin	5.3	Opacity	Transparent
Talc	3.0	Color / oxidation	Clear
Zinc oxide	2.5		
	———		
	100.1		

G 183 Gloss Transparent

Kona feldspar	46.0	Temperature	C/4-6
Colemanite	16.9	Surface @ C/4	Gloss
Barium carbonate	16.5	Fluidity	Little
Flint	10.5	Stain penetration	Yes
Whiting	7.8	Opacity	Transparent
China clay	2.4	Color / oxidation	Clear

100.1

G 184 Clear Gloss

Kona feldspar	45.5	Temperature	C/4-5
Flint	20.0	Surface @ C/4	Gloss
Colemanite	13.3	Fluidity	Fluid
Whiting	8.3	Stain penetration	Yes
Dolomite	6.4	Opacity	Transparent
Zinc oxide	4.0	Color / oxidation	Clear
China clay	2.5		

100.0

G 185 Kona Feldspar Clear

Kona feldspar	43.6	Temperature	C/4-5
Flint	24.7	Surface @ C/4	Gloss
Colemanite	19.8	Fluidity	Some
Barium carbonate	6.4	Stain penetration	Yes
Zinc oxide	3.2	Opacity	Transparent
Whiting	1.5	Color / oxidation	Clear
Kaolin	1.0		

100.2

G 186 Smooth Gloss

Kona feldspar	34.44	Temperature	C/4-6
White lead	25.44	Surface @ C/4	Smooth gloss
Flint	20.90	Fluidity	Some
Whiting	8.11	Stain penetration	Yes
Zinc oxide	5.28	Opacity	Transparent
Dolomite	2.93	Color / oxidation	Clear
Kaolin	2.90		
	100.00		

G 187 Gloss

Kona feldspar	52.7	Temperature	C/4
White lead	19.3	Surface @ C/4	Smooth gloss
Colemanite	12.3	Fluidity	Some
Flint	7.3	Stain penetration	Yes
Dolomite	5.5	Opacity	Transparent
Zinc oxide	2.9	Color / oxidation	Clear, bright
	100.0		

G 188 Semigloss Clear

Potash feldspar	39.6	Temperature	C/4-6
Flint	27.6	Surface @ C/4	Semigloss
Calcined carbonate	16.0	Fluidity	None
Barium carbonate	7.2	Stain penetration	Yes
China clay	6.4	Opacity	Transparent
Zinc oxide	3.2	Color / oxidation	Clear
		Note: Apply medium to heavy	
	100.0		

G 189 Semigloss Clear

Soda feldspar	37.0	Temperature	C/4-6
Flint	23.0	Surface @ C/4	Semigloss
Whiting	20.0	Fluidity	None
Barium carbonate	9.4	Stain penetration	Yes
China clay	6.5	Opacity	Transparent
Zinc oxide	2.5	Color / oxidation	Clear
Dolomite	1.6	Note: Apply thin to medium	
	———		
	100.0		

G 190 Clear Semigloss

Potash feldspar	28	Temperature	C/4-6
Flint	27	Surface @ C/4	Semigloss
China clay	15	Fluidity	Little
Whiting	11	Stain penetration	Yes
Zinc oxide	8	Opacity	Transparent
Dolomite	6	Color / oxidation	Clear
Barium carbonate	5		
	———		
	100		

G 191 Translucent White

Soda feldspar	47.7	Temperature	C/4-8
Flint	22.3	Surface @ C/4	Smooth semigloss
Zinc oxide	7.2	Fluidity	Some
Whiting	7.1	Stain penetration	Yes
Kaolin	5.9	Opacity	Translucent
Kentucky ball #4	4.5	Color / oxidation	White (15)
Barium carbonate	3.0		
Talc	2.3		
	———		
	100.0		

G 192 Translucent

White lead	41.47	Temperature	C/4
Flint	17.69	Surface @ C/4	Semigloss
Soda feldspar	13.65	Fluidity	None
Kaolin	11.80	Stain penetration	Yes
Calcined clay	6.07	Opacity	Translucent
Whiting	4.85	Color / oxidation	Slight white (6)
Tin oxide	4.56		

100.09

G 193 Semigloss

Flint	36.97	Temperature	C/4-6
White lead	28.73	Surface @ C/4	Semigloss
Barium carbonate	12.46	Fluidity	None
China clay	10.97	Stain penetration	Yes
Kona feldspar	6.71	Opacity	Translucent
Dolomite	4.16	Color / oxidation	Slight white (6)

100.00

G 194 White

Potash feldspar	32.7	Temperature	C/4-8
Flint	21.0	Surface @ C/4	Semigloss
Whiting	12.0	Fluidity	Little
Barium carbonate	12.0	Stain penetration	Yes
Zircopax	8.6	Opacity	Translucent
Kaolin	8.6	Color / oxidation	White where thick
Zinc oxide	5.1		(64)

100.0

G 195 Potash Feldspar Semigloss

Potash feldspar	31.6	Temperature	C/4-6
Flint	31.6	Surface @ C/4	Semigloss
White lead	17.1	Fluidity	Little
Whiting	9.2	Stain penetration	Yes
Barium carbonate	5.3	Opacity	Translucent
Ball clay	3.4	Color / oxidation	Slight white (6)
Lithium carbonate	1.8		
	100.0		

G 196 Semimat Opaque

Soda feldspar	47.85	Temperature	C/4-5
Barium carbonate	13.29	Surface @ C/4	Semimat
Whiting	13.29	Fluidity	Some
Colemanite	11.25	Stain penetration	Yes
Flint	10.22	Opacity	Translucent
Zinc oxide	4.10	Color / oxidation	White where thick (32)
	100.00		

G 197 White (Alfred University, Alfred, New York)

Flint	38.2	Temperature	C/4-9
Nepheline syenite	31.8	Surface @ C/4	Semimat
Dolomite	17.5	Fluidity	Little
Kaolin	6.3	Stain penetration	Yes
Whiting	3.4	Opacity	Translucent, thin
Zinc oxide	2.8		Opaque, thick
		Color / oxidation	White (7)
	100.0		

G 198 Translucent Cream

Potash feldspar	36.1	Temperature	C/4-5
White lead	27.7	Surface @ C/4	Semimat
Whiting	18.4	Fluidity	Some
Flint	8.6	Stain penetration	Darks show
Kaolin	6.9	Opacity	Translucent
Calcined kaolin	2.2	Color / oxidation	Cream (16)
	99.9		

G 199 Opaque Semimat

Potash feldspar	26	Temperature	C/4-6
Zircopax	17	Surface @ C/4	Semimat
Flint	16	Fluidity	Little
Whiting	10	Stain penetration	Darks show
Zinc oxide	9	Opacity	Opaque
China clay	8	Color / oxidation	White (32)
Dolomite	7		
Barium carbonate	7		
	100		

G 200 Mat

Potash feldspar	30.0	Temperature	C/4-6
Zinc oxide	30.0	Surface @ C/4	Dry mat
Flint	18.0	Fluidity	None
Whiting	8.0	Stain penetration	Yes
Barium	7.3	Opacity	Translucent
China clay	5.4	Color / oxidation	Whitish
Dolomite	1.3		
	100.0		

G 201 Light Yellow

Potash feldspar	30.3	Temperature	C/4-5
Flint	20.2	Surface @ C/4	Gloss
Colemanite	20.2	Fluidity	Little
Kaolin	10.2	Stain penetration	Yes
Dolomite	10.0	Opacity	Translucent
Yellow stain	5.1	Color / oxidation	Light yellow (4)
Tin oxide	3.0	Note: Use over white clay	
	———		
	99.0		

G 202 Pink Opaque

Potash feldspar	24.7	Temperature	C/4-6
Flint	23.7	Surface @ C/4	Semigloss
Kaolin	13.8	Fluidity	Little
Whiting	10.7	Stain penetration	Darks show
Pink stain	10.5	Opacity	Opaque
Zinc oxide	6.8	Color / oxidation	Light pink (44)
Barium carbonate	4.9	Note: Use over white clay	
Dolomite	4.9		
	———		
	100.0		

G 203 Copper Red Reduction (Alfred University, Alfred, New York)

Flint	30.90	Temperature	C/4-9
Soda feldspar	27.21	Surface @ C/4	Gloss
Whiting	12.88	Fluidity	Little
Frit #3195	11.81	Stain penetration	None
Zircopax	7.94	Opacity	Opaque
Kaolin	5.54	Color / reduction	Deep red, black
Dolomite	1.97		areas (135)
Zinc oxide	.86		
Copper oxide	.79		
	———		
	99.90		

G 204 Reduction Rust (Alfred University, Alfred, New York)

Cornwall stone	60.49	Temperature	C/4-8
Flint	18.09	Surface @ C/4	Semigloss
Whiting	11.99	Fluidity	None
Red iron oxide	7.41	Stain penetration	None
Kaolin	2.02	Opacity	Opaque
		Color / reduction	Rust (78)
	100.00		

G 205 Red Rust

Soda feldspar	28.62	Temperature	C/4-7
Flint	22.20	Surface @ C/4	Gloss
Tin oxide	16.29	Fluidity	Little
Whiting	11.82	Stain penetration	None
Red iron oxide	7.55	Opacity	Opaque
White lead	7.55	Color / oxidation	Red rust (49)
Kaolin	5.30	Note: Apply thin to medium	
	99.33		

G 206 Jade Green

Potash feldspar	38.1	Temperature	C/4-6
Barium carbonate	19.0	Surface @ C/4	Semimat
Kaolin	9.6	Fluidity	Some
Flint	9.5	Stain penetration	None
Colemanite	9.5	Opacity	Opaque
Zinc oxide	9.4	Color / oxidation	Jade green
Copper carbonate	4.9		(130)
	100.0		

G 207 Semigloss Black

Potash feldspar	32	Temperature	C/4-7
Barium carbonate	16	Surface @ C/4	Semigloss
Bernard clay	16	Fluidity	None
Kaolin	8	Stain penetration	None
Zinc oxide	8	Opacity	Opaque
Flint	7	Color / oxidation	Black (146)
Colemanite	7		
Copper oxide	3		
Cobalt oxide	2		
Iron oxide	2		
	101		

G 208 Black Gold Fleck

Frit #IV48	75.24	Temperature	C/4-5
Red iron oxide	15.24	Surface @ C/4	Smooth gloss
Kaolin	9.52	Fluidity	Some
	100.00	Stain penetration	None
		Opacity	Opaque
		Color / oxidation	Deep black, some gold fleck (113)

Note: Black stain breaks through surface as lustrous dark brown

Stoneware Glaze Formulas   Cone/5-10

Glazes that mature in the temperature range of 2185° to 2390°F. are called stoneware glazes. These and higher firing temperatures impose a limitation on the possible glaze color range. Often the colors are not as bright but rather more subtle compared to the lower-temperature glazes. Within the subtle range of colors, however, there are tremendous glaze and color possibilities—muted whites, grays, tans, and other earth colors. Stoneware is popular also for its surface quality of dense smoothness, butter finish, and translucent depths that reveal the handmade process.

Many stoneware formulas contain only a few materials, which permits faster and easier measuring and mixing. Thus, the ceramist does not need a large chemical inventory and can make many glazes at lower cost in less time. This brings up a critical point: that no matter how well the ceramic form is designed and made, the form will be lost from improper measuring, mixing, or application of the glaze. Craftsmanship in measuring, mixing, and applying the glaze is essential. It is all too easy to misread a formula and bungle the glaze.

The formulas that follow are organized into five temperature groups; subdivided as to gloss, semigloss, and mat surfaces; then distinguished as to transparent, translucent, and opaque qualities; and followed by color and special effects.

CONE/5

G 209 Ford's Clear Gloss

Potash feldspar	50.98	Temperature	C/5-9
Whiting	19.61	Surface @ C/5	Gloss
Kaolin	9.80	Fluidity	Some
Zinc oxide	8.82	Stain penetration	Yes
Flint	5.88	Opacity	Transparent
Bentonite	4.91	Color / oxidation	Clear
	———	Note: Some cracks	
	100.00		

G 210 Bright Gloss

Colemanite	50.0	Temperature	C/5-7
Flint	32.5	Surface @ C/5	Gloss
Kaolin	17.5	Fluidity	None
	———	Stain penetration	Yes
	100.0	Opacity	Transparent
		Color / oxidation	Clear, bright

G 211 Glossy

Colemanite	47	Temperature	C/5
P.V. kaolin	47	Surface @ C/5	Gloss
Zircopax	6	Fluidity	Some
	———	Stain penetration	Yes
	100	Opacity	Transparent
		Color / oxidation	Clear

G 212 Frit #25 Gloss

Potash feldspar	34.9	Temperature	C/5-7
Frit #25	25.3	Surface @ C/5	Gloss
Flint	25.3	Fluidity	Little
Whiting	5.8	Stain penetration	Yes
Colemanite	5.1	Opacity	Transparent
Kentucky ball #4	3.6	Color / oxidation	Clear
	———		
	100.0		

Copper carbonate	3.0	Color / oxidation	Turquoise
Iron chromate	3.0	Color / oxidation	Gray-blue
Rutile	3.0	Color / oxidation	Tan
Copper carbonate	3.0 }	Color / oxidation	Blue-green
Cobalt carbonate	.5 }		

G 213 Gloss Colemanite

P.V. kaolin	44	Temperature	C/5-6
Colemanite	28	Surface @ C/5	Gloss
Wollastonite	20	Fluidity	Some
Potash feldspar	8	Stain penetration	Yes
	——	Opacity	Translucent
	100	Color / oxidation	Whitish (6)
Red iron oxide	5	Color / oxidation	Tan (28)

G 214 Gloss Translucent

Potash feldspar	37.81	Temperature	C/5-7
Silica	22.04	Surface @ C/5	Gloss
Colemanite	17.04	Fluidity	Some
Zinc oxide	8.12	Stain penetration	Yes
Barium carbonate	6.58	Opacity	Translucent
Talc	6.25	Color / oxidation	White (7)
Tin oxide	2.00		
	———		
	99.84		

G 215 ML 2A Gloss

Potash feldspar	32.44	Temperature	C/5-6
Silica	30.58	Surface @ C/5	Gloss
Colemanite	14.69	Fluidity	Some
Zinc oxide	8.61	Stain penetration	Yes
Barium carbonate	6.98	Opacity	Translucent
Talc	6.70	Color / oxidation	Bright blue-white (32)
	———		
	100.00		

G 216 Gloss Opaque

P.V. kaolin	50	Temperature	C/5-6
Colemanite	30	Surface @ C/5	Gloss
Wollastonite	20	Fluidity	Fluid
	——	Stain penetration	Yes
	100	Opacity	Opaque
		Color / oxidation	White (32)
Rutile	2	Color / oxidation	Spotty tan (24)
Ilmenite	2		

G 217 Semigloss Transparent

Potash feldspar	53.0	Temperature	C/5-6
Flint	18.5	Surface @ C/5	Semigloss
Barium carbonate	13.0	Fluidity	None
Whiting	6.5	Stain penetration	Yes
Kentucky ball #4	4.5	Opacity	Transparent
Kaolin	4.5	Color / oxidation	Clear
	100.0		

G 218 Off-white (Alfred University, Alfred, New York)

Soda feldspar	46.75	Temperature	C/5-9
Flint	15.22	Surface @ C/5	Semigloss
Talc	13.76	Fluidity	Little
Colemanite	11.65	Stain penetration	Yes
Dolomite	8.09	Opacity	Transparent
Kaolin	4.53	Color / oxidation	White where thick
	100.00		

G 219 Semigloss White

Soda feldspar	56.85	Temperature	C/5-8
Barium carbonate	14.64	Surface @ C/5	Semigloss
White lead	7.21	Fluidity	None
Kaolin	6.87	Stain penetration	Yes
Flint	5.01	Opacity	Translucent
Whiting	4.33	Color / oxidation	White (6)
Zircopax	4.24		
Zinc oxide	.85		

100.00

G 220 Translucent Semigloss

Potash feldspar	53.0	Temperature	C/5-6
Flint	18.5	Surface @ C/5	Semigloss
Barium carbonate	13.0	Fluidity	Little
Whiting	6.5	Stain penetration	Yes
Kentucky ball #4	4.5	Opacity	Translucent
Kaolin	4.5	Color / oxidation	Grayed white (152)

100.0

Chromium oxide	3.2	Color / oxidation	Gray-green (139)
Tin oxide	5.2		

G 221 Semigloss

Potash feldspar	32.8	Temperature	C/5-8
Flint	22.2	Surface @ C/5	Semigloss
Whiting	12.0	Fluidity	Little
Barium carbonate	12.0	Stain penetration	Yes
Kaolin	8.0	Opacity	Translucent
Zircopax	8.0	Color / oxidation	Slight white (6)
Zinc oxide	5.0		

100.0

G 222 Frit #14 Semigloss

Flint	50.9	Temperature	C/5-9
Potash feldspar	13.9	Surface @ C/5	Semigloss
Frit #14	13.9	Fluidity	None
Kentucky ball #4	9.3	Stain penetration	Darks show
Bentonite	6.0	Opacity	Opaque
Opax	6.0	Color / oxidation	White (64)
	100.0		

G 223 Semimat White

almost *test glaze # 7*

Nepheline syenite	50.9	Temperature	C/5-7
Whiting	19.5	Surface @ C/5	Semimat
Flint	18.0	Fluidity	Little
Kaolin	9.0	Stain penetration	Little
Zinc oxide	2.6	Opacity	Translucent where thick
		Color / oxidation	Whitish (32)
	100.0		
Copper carbonate	2.0	Color / oxidation	Gray-green
Manganese dioxide	4.0	Color / oxidation	Gray-violet
Red iron oxide	5.0	Color / oxidation	Medium brown
Rutile	10.0	Color / oxidation	Tan

G 224 L.A. Mat

White lead	41.45	Temperature	C/5-6
Potash feldspar	26.38	Surface @ C/5	Semimat
Calcined kaolin	10.80	Fluidity	Little
E.P. kaolin	6.28	Stain penetration	Yes
Whiting	6.28	Opacity	Translucent
Silica	5.67	Color / oxidation	Egg shell white (30)
Zinc oxide	3.14		
	100.00		

change #2 diff measures.

G 225 Satin Mat

Potash feldspar	39.0	Temperature	C/5-6
Zinc oxide	25.0	Surface @ C/5	Semimat
Whiting	16.1	Fluidity	Little
Flint	14.2	Stain penetration	Yes
Kaolin	6.7	Opacity	Translucent
	——	Color / oxidation	Slight white (6)
	101.0		

G 226 White Mat

Potash feldspar	54.0	Temperature	C/5-7
China clay	14.1	Surface @ C/5	Smooth mat
Whiting	14.0	Fluidity	None
Barium carbonate	6.0	Stain penetration	Darks show
Flint	5.8	Opacity	Opaque
Zinc oxide	4.0	Color / oxidation	White (7)
Magnesium carbonate	2.1		
	——		
	100.0		

G 227 Clear Mat

Red lead	50.0	Temperature	C/5-6
Potash feldspar	18.1	Surface @ C/5	Mat
Kaolin	11.0	Fluidity	Little
Kentucky ball #4	10.0	Stain penetration	Yes
Whiting	6.3	Opacity	Transparent
Flint	4.6	Color/oxidation	Off-white (4)
	——		
	100.0		

Cobalt oxide	4		
Uranium oxide	13	Color / oxidation	Opaque, black, spots of metallic (145)
Cobalt carbonate	.3		
Uranium oxide	1.3	Color / oxidation	Yellow-green (144)

G 228 Translucent Mat-A

Potash feldspar	39.3	Temperature	C/5-7
White lead	17.8	Surface @ C/5	Mat
Kaolin	17.4	Fluidity	None
Dolomite	12.7	Stain penetration	Yes
Whiting	7.0	Opacity	Translucent
Flint	5.8	Color / oxidation	White (6)
	100.0		

G 229 Smooth Mat

Kona feldspar	63.10	Temperature	C/5-6
Whiting	12.71	Surface @ C/5	Smooth mat
Barium carbonate	10.04	Fluidity	Some
Flint	7.36	Stain penetration	Yes
Kaolin	6.79	Opacity	Translucent
		Color / oxidation	Spotty white (7)
	100.00		

G 230 Cream Mat

White lead	33.01	Temperature	C/5-7
Kentucky ball #4	33.01	Surface @ C/5	Mat
Potash feldspar	17.95	Fluidity	None
Whiting	16.03	Stain penetration	Yes
		Opacity	Translucent
	100.00	Color / oxidation	Cream (30)

G 231 Opaque Mat

Potash feldspar	38.28	Temperature	C/5-7
Kaolin	14.88	Surface @ C/5	Dry mat
Zircopax	13.20	Fluidity	None
Barium carbonate	10.00	Stain penetration	Darks show
Flint	8.92	Opacity	Opaque
Whiting	8.92	Color / oxidation	White (32)
Zinc oxide	3.88		
Talc	1.92		

100.00

G 232 Semimat Yellow

Potash feldspar	53.0	Temperature	C/5-7
Flint	18.5	Surface @ C/5	Semimat
Barium carbonate	13.0	Fluidity	Little
Zinc oxide	6.5	Stain penetration	Yes
Uranium oxide, yellow	6.0	Opacity	Translucent
Kentucky ball #4	4.5	Color / oxidation	Yellow (5)
Kaolin	4.5	Note: Use on white clay	

106.0

G 233 Semigloss Tan

Potash feldspar	36.1	Temperature	C/5-7
Flint	25.6	Surface @ C/5	Semigloss
E.P. kaolin	17.1	Fluidity	Little
Whiting	14.6	Stain penetration	Yes
Talc	2.7	Opacity	Transparent
Red iron oxide	1.6	Color / oxidation	Warm tan (28)
Rutile	1.4		
Bone ash	.9		

100.0

G 234 Opaque Brown Mat-A

Potash feldspar	33.2	Temperature	C/5-6
White lead	15.0	Surface @ C/5	Smooth mat
Kaolin	14.7	Fluidity	Little
Albany slip	14.0	Stain penetration	Darks show
Dolomite	10.7	Opacity	Opaque
Whiting	5.9	Color / oxidation	Tan-brown, dark
Flint	5.0		specks (23)
Ilmenite	1.5		
	100.0		

G 235 Yellow-ochre

Kaolin	29.20	Temperature	C/5-7
Frit #5301	25.40	Surface @ C/5	Mat
Zinc oxide	17.09	Fluidity	Little
Flint	15.69	Stain penetration	Very darks show
Red iron oxide	4.27	Opacity	Opaque
Lithium carbonate	3.74	Color / oxidation	Spotty yellow-
Tin oxide	3.74		ochre (28)
Yellow ochre	.50		
Copper carbonate	.37		
	100.00		

CONE/6

G 236 Bright Clear Gloss

Cornwall stone	37.7	Temperature	C/6
Red lead	37.7	Surface @ C/6	Gloss
Flint	18.8	Fluidity	Little
Whiting	5.8	Stain penetration	Yes
	——	Opacity	Transparent
	100.0	Color / oxidation	Bright clear

Note: Apply medium thickness

G 237 Transparent Gloss

Soda feldspar	35.6	Temperature	C/6-8
China clay	15.2	Surface @ C/6	Gloss
Dolomite	11.0	Fluidity	Some
Spodumene	9.9	Stain penetration	Yes
Whiting	8.3	Opacity	Transparent
Flint	6.9	Color / oxidation	Clear
Barium carbonate	5.4		
Kentucky ball #4	3.9		
Zinc oxide	2.1		
Talc	1.7		
	——		
	100.0		

G 238 Clear Semigloss

Potash feldspar	54.4	Temperature	C/6-7
Red lead	32.6	Surface @ C/6	Semigloss
Flint	10.8	Fluidity	Little
Cornwall stone	2.2	Stain penetration	Yes
	——	Opacity	Transparent
	100.0	Color / oxidation	Bright clear

G 239 Semigloss

Soda feldspar	45.15	Temperature	C/6-8
Flint	20.54	Surface @ C/6	Semigloss
Barium carbonate	8.47	Fluidity	Little
Zinc oxide	6.88	Stain penetration	Yes
Whiting	6.77	Opacity	Transparent
Kaolin	5.64	Color / oxidation	Whitish where thick
Kentucky ball #4	4.29		(6)
Talc	2.26		
	100.00		

G 240 Translucent Semigloss

Potash feldspar	70	Temperature	C/6-8
Whiting	13	Surface @ C/6	Semigloss
Flint	8	Fluidity	Little
Cornwall stone	7	Stain penetration	Yes
Zinc oxide	2	Opacity	Translucent
		Color / oxidation	White (6)
	100	Note: Cracks	

G 241 Semigloss

Soda feldspar	50	Temperature	C/6-8
Soda ash	28	Surface @ C/6	Semigloss
Flint	11	Fluidity	Some
Whiting	10	Stain penetration	Some
Borax	1	Opacity	Translucent
		Color / oxidation	Some white where
	100		thick

G 242 White Cornwall Stone

Cornwall stone	40	Temperature	C/6-8
Potash feldspar	25	Surface @ C/6	Semigloss
Whiting	13	Fluidity	Little
Kentucky ball #4	12	Stain penetration	Yes
Flint	5	Opacity	Translucent
Zinc oxide	5	Color / oxidation	Whitish (7)
	100		

G 243 Soda Feldspar White

Soda feldspar	37	Temperature	C/6-7
Flint	23	Surface @ C/6	Semigloss
Georgia clay	20	Fluidity	Some
Whiting	12	Stain penetration	Yes
Talc	6	Opacity	Translucent
Zinc oxide	2	Color / oxidation	White (16)
	100		

G 244 White

Potash feldspar	36.82	Temperature	C/6-8
Spodumene	19.90	Surface @ C/6	Semigloss
Flint	18.04	Fluidity	Some
Colemanite	10.95	Stain penetration	Yes
Talc	10.54	Opacity	Translucent
Boric acid	3.75	Color / oxidation	Whitish (7)
	100.00		

G 245 Semigloss White

Soda feldspar	86.32	Temperature	C/6-8
Kentucky ball #4	6.74	Surface @ C/6	Semigloss
Whiting	2.83	Fluidity	None
Zinc oxide	2.40	Stain penetration	Darks show
Flint	1.71	Opacity	Opaque
	——	Color / oxidation	White (32)
	100.00	Note: Apply thin and even coat	

test #2

G 246 Satin Mat

Potash feldspar	50.7	Temperature	C/6-7
Whiting	19.5	Surface @ C/6	Semimat
Flint	18.5	Fluidity	Little
Kaolin	8.8	Stain penetration	Yes
Zinc oxide	2.5	Opacity	Translucent
	——	Color / oxidation	Slight white (32)
	100.0		

G 247 Semimat

Soda feldspar	42.5	Temperature	C/6-8
Kaolin	16.3	Surface @ C/6	Semimat
Flint	14.0	Fluidity	Little
Barium carbonate	11.0	Stain penetration	Yes
Whiting	9.8	Opacity	Translucent
Zinc oxide	4.3	Color / oxidation	Some white (6)
Talc	2.1		
	——		
	100.0		

test glaze #3

G 248 Translucent Mat

Potash feldspar	46.24	Temperature	C/6-8
Barium carbonate	23.60	Surface @ C/6	Smooth mat
Kentucky ball #4	11.21	Fluidity	No
Whiting	9.95	Stain penetration	Yes
Zinc oxide	9.00	Opacity	Translucent
	——	Color / oxidation	Cream-white (6)
	100.00		

G 249 Opaque Mat

Potash feldspar	35	Temperature	C/6-8
Flint	24	Surface @ C/6	Mat
Whiting	18	Fluidity	No
Zinc oxide	11	Stain penetration	Darks show
Kentucky ball #4	8	Opacity	Opaque
Zircopax	4	Color / oxidation	White (32)
	100		

G 250 Reduction Blood Red

Flint	29.56	Temperature	C/6-7
Borax	29.36	Surface @ C/6	Gloss
Red lead	20.39	Fluidity	Little
Whiting	6.12	Stain penetration	Yes
Boric acid	4.69	Opacity	Translucent
Soda ash	4.08	Color / reduction	Reddish to blood red
Kaolin	3.06		(66/62)
Tin oxide	1.94		
Copper carbonate	.80		
	100.00		

change of # x measured

G 251 Persimmon

Flint	36.5	Temperature	C/6-8
Potash feldspar	30.0	Surface @ C/6	Gloss
Whiting	15.0	Fluidity	Some
Red iron oxide	11.5	Stain penetration	No
Kaolin	7.5	Opacity	Opaque
	100.5	Color / oxidation	Dark brown (156)

G 252 Green-black

Spodumene	35.57	Temperature	C/6
Frit #25	24.53	Surface @ C/6	Gloss
Kaolin	15.94	Fluidity	Some
Colemanite	13.49	Stain penetration	Yes
Tin oxide	6.13	Opacity	Transparent
Copper carbonate	4.34	Color / oxidation	Gray green,
			metallic areas (143)
	100.00	Note: Brown-black over undercolors	

CONE/7

G 253 Clear Gloss

White lead	28	Temperature	C/7-9
Kona feldspar	28	Surface @ C/7	Gloss
Flint	22	Fluidity	None
E.P. kaolin	12	Stain penetration	Yes
Whiting	10	Opacity	Transparent
	——	Color / oxidation	Clear
	100		

G 254 Translucent Gloss

Potash feldspar	29.63	Temperature	C/7-9
Flint	22.22	Surface @ C/7	Gloss
Whiting	22.22	Fluidity	None
Kaolin	11.11	Stain penetration	Yes
Zinc oxide	7.41	Opacity	Translucent
Titanium dioxide	7.41	Color / oxidation	Tan (40)
	——		
	100.00		

G 255 White Gloss

Potash feldspar	29.8	Temperature	C/7-9
Flint	25.5	Surface @ C/7	Gloss
Calcium carbonate	15.7	Fluidity	Some
Tin oxide	8.2	Stain penetration	Darks show
Barium carbonate	7.6	Opacity	Opaque
China clay	7.6	Color / oxidation	White (48)
Zinc oxide	5.6		
	——		
	100.0		

G 256 Semigloss

Flint	39	Temperature	C/7-9
Potash feldspar	32	Surface @ C/7	Semigloss
Calcium carbonate	18	Fluidity	None
Kaolin	11	Stain penetration	Yes
	___	Opacity	Translucent
	100	Color / oxidation	Cream-white (6)

G 257 White Semimat

Potash feldspar	66	Temperature	C/7-9
Zinc oxide	12	Surface @ C/7	Semimat
Whiting	12	Fluidity	None
Kentucky ball #4	10	Stain penetration	Yes
	___	Opacity	Translucent
	100	Color / oxidation	White (6)

G 258 Mat Opaque

Potash feldspar	36.0	Temperature	C/7-9
Flint	29.2	Surface @ C/7	Mat
Calcium carbonate	13.0	Fluidity	None
China clay	7.9	Stain penetration	Yes
Tin oxide	5.9	Opacity	Translucent when thin
Zinc oxide	5.0		Opaque when thick
Dolomite	3.2	Color / oxidation	White (63)
	_____		
	100.2		

G 259 White Opaque Mat

Potash feldspar	49	Temperature	C/7-10
Kaolin	27	Surface @ C/7	Dry mat
Whiting	20	Fluidity	None
Spodumene	4	Stain penetration	Darks show
	——	Opacity	Opaque
	100	Color / oxidation	White (32)

G 260 White Mat

Potash feldspar	49	Temperature	C/7-10
Whiting	26	Surface @ C/7	Dry mat
Kaolin	18	Fluidity	None
Spodumene	7	Stain penetration	Very darks show
	——	Opacity	Opaque
	100	Color / oxidation	White (32)

G 261 Cream Mat

Potash feldspar	47	Temperature	C/7-9
Kentucky ball #4	24	Surface @ C/7	Dry mat
Whiting	22	Fluidity	None
Spodumene	5	Stain penetration	Darks show
Whiting	2	Opacity	Opaque
	——	Color / oxidation	Cream (15)
	100		

CONE/8

G 262 Clear Gloss (Phil Denin, University of Illinois, Urbana, Illinois)

Potash feldspar	63.6	Temperature	C/8-11
Colemanite	27.3	Surface @ C/8	Gloss
Kaolin	9.1	Fluidity	Some
	———	Stain penetration	Yes
	100.0	Opacity	Transparent
		Color / oxidation	Clear

G 263 Gloss

Potash feldspar	58	Temperature	C/8
Whiting	11	Surface @ C/8	Gloss
Zinc oxide	11	Fluidity	Fluid
Flint	10	Stain penetration	Yes
Kentucky ball #4	8	Opacity	Transparent
Kaolin	2	Color / oxidation	Clear
	———	Note: Cracks	
	100		

G 264 Transparent Gloss

Potash feldspar	46.49	Temperature	C/8
Whiting	16.67	Surface @ C/8	Gloss
Zinc oxide	12.28	Fluidity	Fluid
Flint	11.40	Stain penetration	Yes
Kaolin	8.77	Opacity	Transparent, thin
Tin oxide	2.63	Color / oxidation	White (7)
Rutile	1.76	/ reduction	Tan (35)
	———		
	100.00		

G 265 Clear

Potash feldspar	37.4	Temperature	C/8-9
Whiting	18.7	Surface @ C/8	Gloss
Cornwall stone	18.7	Fluidity	Fluid
Kentucky ball #4	18.7	Stain penetration	Yes
Zinc oxide	6.5	Opacity	Transparent
	———	Color / oxidation	Clear
	100.0	/ reduction	Clear
		Note: Cracks	

G 266 Off-white Gloss

Flint	32	Temperature	C/8-9
Potash feldspar	31	Surface @ C/8	Gloss
Colemanite	13	Fluidity	Some
Whiting	9	Stain penetration	Some
Barium carbonate	8	Opacity	Translucent
Kaolin	5	Color / oxidation	Off-white (16)
Magnesium carbonate	3	/ reduction	Off-white (7)
	———		
	101		

G 267 Gloss

Potash feldspar	29.2	Temperature	C/8-9
Flint	28.1	Surface @ C/8	Gloss
Kaolin	15.0	Fluidity	Little
Calcium carbonate	11.1	Stain penetration	Yes
Zinc oxide	6.1	Opacity	Translucent
Dolomite	5.9	Color / oxidation	Off-white (6)
Barium carbonate	4.6	/ reduction	Off-white (7)
	———		
	100.0		

G 268 Translucent

Potash feldspar	28.5	Temperature	C/8-9
Flint	27.4	Surface @ C/8	Gloss
Kaolin	14.6	Fluidity	Little
Calcium carbonate	10.8	Stain penetration	Darks show
Zinc oxide	6.0	Opacity	Translucent
Dolomite	5.8	Color / oxidation	White (7)
Barium carbonate	4.4	/ reduction	White (8)
Tin oxide	2.5		
	100.0		

G 269 Gloss

Spodumene	23.1	Temperature	C/8-9
Potash feldspar	20.3	Surface @ C/8	Gloss
Lepidolite	18.8	Fluidity	Very fluid
Whiting	13.0	Stain penetration	Some
Colemanite	12.0	Opacity	Translucent
Cryolite	6.7	Color / oxidation	Off-white (6)
Bone ash	6.1	/ reduction	White (7)
	100.0		

G 270 Cornwall Stone Semigloss

Cornwall stone	83	Temperature	C/8-9
Whiting	14	Surface @ C/8	Semigloss
Spodumene	3	Fluidity	Little
		Stain penetration	Yes
	100	Opacity	Translucent
		Color / oxidation	Off-white (15)
		/ reduction	Off-white (7)

G 271 White Semigloss

Potash feldspar	80	Temperature	C/8-9
Whiting	10	Surface @ C/8	Semigloss
Flint	10	Fluidity	None
	———	Stain penetration	Darks show
	100	Opacity	Translucent
		Color / oxidation	White (7)
		/ reduction	Off-white (7)
		Note: Crackle	

G 272 Semigloss

Potash feldspar	78.43	Temperature	C/8-10
Whiting	9.80	Surface @ C/8	Semigloss
Kaolin	9.80	Fluidity	None
Bone ash	1.97	Stain penetration	Yes
	———	Opacity	Translucent
	100.00	Color / oxidation	Slight white (6)

G 273 Volcanic Ash Semigloss

Volcanic ash	56	Temperature	C/8-9
Whiting	13	Surface @ C/8	Semigloss
Flint	10	Fluidity	Little
Potash feldspar	10	Stain penetration	Yes
Bentonite	4	Opacity	Transparent
Kaolin	3	Color / oxidation	Slight yellow (15)
Bone ash	2		
Talc	2		
	———		
	100		

G 274 Soda Feldspar Semigloss

Soda feldspar	44	Temperature	C/8-10
Flint	35	Surface @ C/8	Semigloss
Whiting	14	Fluidity	None
Kaolin	7	Stain penetration	Darks show
	———	Opacity	Translucent
	100	Color / oxidation	White (7)
		/ reduction	Off-white (8)

G 275 White Semigloss

Cornwall stone	42.7	Temperature	C/8-9
Flint	26.7	Surface @ C/8	Semigloss
Kaolin	13.7	Fluidity	Little
Whiting	10.9	Stain penetration	Darks show
Dolomite	4.5	Opacity	Translucent
Zinc oxide	1.5	Color / oxidation	Off-white (15)
	——	/ reduction	White (7)
	100.0		

G 276 Clear Semigloss

Kona feldspar	42.6	Temperature	C/8-9
Whiting	17.3	Surface @ C/8	Semigloss
Calcined clay	13.0	Fluidity	Fluid
Flint	8.7	Stain penetration	Yes
Colemanite	8.6	Opacity	Transparent
Barium carbonate	5.9	Color / oxidation	Clear
Kaolin	4.0	/ reduction	Clear
	——		
	100.1		

G 277 Ivory White Semigloss

Potash feldspar	39.6	Temperature	C/8-9
Flint	27.6	Surface @ C/8	Semigloss
Calcium carbonate	16.0	Fluidity	Little
Barium carbonate	7.2	Stain penetration	Yes
Kaolin	6.4	Opacity	Translucent
Zinc oxide	3.2	Color / oxidation	White (6)
	——	/ reduction	White (7)
	100.0		

G 278 Semigloss Opaque

Potash feldspar	54.3	Temperature	C/8-9
Flint	17.6	Surface @ C/8	Semigloss
Whiting	12.0	Fluidity	Little
Volcanic ash	9.4	Stain penetration	Darks show
Kaolin	3.5	Opacity	Opaque
Rutile	3.2	Color / oxidation	Tan (21)
	———	/ reduction	Tan (19)
	100.0		

G 279 Opaque

Potash feldspar	40.0	Temperature	C/8-10
Flint	21.8	Surface @ C/8	Semigloss
Whiting	18.0	Fluidity	Little
Calcined kaolin	8.7	Stain penetration	Darks show
E.P. kaolin	8.6	Opacity	Opaque
Spodumene	2.9	Color / oxidation	White (31)
	———	/ reduction	White (7)
	100.0		

G 280 Semigloss White

Potash feldspar	35.0	Temperature	C/8-10
Zircopax	24.3	Surface @ C/8	Semigloss
Flint	16.2	Fluidity	Little
Whiting	14.5	Stain penetration	None
E.P. kaolin	10.0	Opacity	Opaque
	———	Color / oxidation	White (32)
	100.0	/ reduction	White (32)

G 281 White

Potash feldspar	34.3	Temperature	C/8-10
Flint	34.2	Surface @ C/8	Semigloss
Dolomite	15.8	Fluidity	Little
Kaolin	9.0	Stain penetration	Darks show
Whiting	6.0	Opacity	Opaque
Zinc oxide	.7	Color / oxidation	White (6)
	——	/ reduction	White (7)
	100.0		

G 282 Transparent Semimat

Potash feldspar	46.51	Temperature	C/8-9
Zinc oxide	23.26	Surface @ C/8	Semimat
Whiting	16.28	Fluidity	Fluid
Flint	13.95	Stain penetration	Yes
	——	Opacity	Transparent, thin
	100.00		Translucent, thick
		Color / oxidation	White (7)
		/ reduction	White (7)

G 283 Semimat

Potash feldspar	46.90	Temperature	C/8-9
Zinc oxide	28.56	Surface @ C/8	Semimat
Flint	11.84	Fluidity	Some
Whiting	9.10	Stain penetration	Yes
Rutile	3.60	Opacity	Translucent
	——	Color / oxidation	White (31)
	100.00	/ reduction	Brown (146)

G 284 Nepheline Syenite Semimat

Nepheline syenite	44	Temperature	C/8-10
Flint	26	Surface @ C/8	Semimat
E.P. kaolin	20	Fluidity	Little
Whiting	10	Stain penetration	Darks show
	____	Opacity	Translucent
	100	Color / oxidation	White (7)
		/ reduction	Off-white (8)

G 285 Semimat

Potash feldspar	41.6	Temperature	C/8-10
Whiting	18.5	Surface @ C/8	Semimat
Cornwall stone	18.5	Fluidity	Little
Kentucky ball #4	18.5	Stain penetration	Darks show
Zinc oxide	2.9	Opacity	Translucent
	____	Color / oxidation	White (15)
	100.0	/ reduction	White (7)

G 286 Off-white

Potash feldspar	39	Temperature	C/8-10
Flint	29	Surface @ C/8	Semimat
Whiting	19	Fluidity	None
Kaolin	10	Stain penetration	Darks show
Zinc oxide	4	Opacity	Translucent
	____	Color / oxidation	White (64)
	101	/ reduction	Off-white (8)

G 287 Opaque Semimat

Potash feldspar	50.4	Temperature	C/8-11
Flint	24.9	Surface @ C/8	Semimat
Whiting	17.3	Fluidity	None
China clay	3.7	Stain penetration	Darks show
Dolomite	2.6	Opacity	Opaque
Zinc oxide	1.1	Color / oxidation	White (32)
	____	/ reduction	White (7)
	100.0		

G 288 Opaque Semimat

Potash feldspar	42.86	Temperature	C/8-10
Flint	19.05	Surface @ C/8	Semimat
Talc	14.29	Fluidity	Little
Colemanite	12.39	Stain penetration	None
Dolomite	6.67	Opacity	Opaque
Kaolin	4.74	Color / oxidation	White (6)
	——	/ reduction	White (32)
	100.00		

G 289 Opaque White

Potash feldspar	40	Temperature	C/8-10
Whiting	20	Surface @ C/8	Semimat
Cornwall stone	20	Fluidity	None
Kentucky ball #4	20	Stain penetration	Darks show
Zinc oxide	2	Opacity	Opaque
	——	Color / oxidation	White (6)
	102	/ reduction	Gray (151)

G 290 Opaque

Potash feldspar	39	Temperature	C/8-10
Mixed hardwood ashes	37	Surface @ C/8	Semimat
Kentucky ball #4	19	Fluidity	Some
Spodumene	5	Stain penetration	None
	——	Opacity	Opaque
	100	Color / oxidation	Tan (158)
		/ reduction	Tan (28)

G 291 Opaque White

Potash feldspar	33	Temperature	C/8-10
Flint	31	Surface @ C/8	Semimat
Whiting	20	Fluidity	None
Kaolin	14	Stain penetration	Darks show
Spodumene	2	Opacity	Opaque
	——	Color / oxidation	White (32)
	100	/ reduction	White (7)
		Note: Some cracks	

G 292 Translucent Mat

White lead	40.91	Temperature	C/8-9
Potash feldspar	27.27	Surface @ C/9	Smooth mat
Kaolin	13.64	Fluidity	Some
Whiting	9.09	Stain penetration	Darks show
Flint	4.54	Opacity	Translucent
Zinc oxide	2.72	Color / oxidation	Off-white (15)
Bentonite	1.83		
	100.00		

G 293 MG 2 (Alfred University, Alfred, New York)

Potash feldspar	41.6	Temperature	C/8-10
Flint	20.1	Surface @ C/9	Mat
Talc	14.6	Fluidity	Little
Colemanite	11.9	Stain penetration	Darks show
Dolomite	7.6	Opacity	Opaque
Kaolin	4.2	Color / oxidation	White (32)
		/ reduction	White (7)
	100.0		

G 294 Zinc Oxide Mat

Zinc oxide	41.22	Temperature	C/8-9
Potash feldspar	22.68	Surface @ C/8	Mat
Flint	17.07	Fluidity	None
Whiting	13.17	Stain penetration	Darks show
Rutile	5.86	Opacity	Opaque
		Color / oxidation	Warm tan (38)
	100.00	/ reduction	Tan (23)

G 295 White Mat

Potash feldspar	39.44	Temperature	C/8-9
Flint	18.78	Surface @ C/8	Mat
Talc	14.08	Fluidity	None
Colemanite	11.27	Stain penetration	Darks show
Dolomite	7.51	Opacity	Opaque
Kentucky ball #4	4.69	Color / oxidation	White (32)
Kaolin	3.76	/ reduction	White (32)
Bentonite	.47		
	100.00		

G 296 Mat

Potash feldspar	64	Temperature	C/8-9
Kaolin	24	Surface @ C/8	Dry mat
Whiting	8	Fluidity	None
Zinc oxide	4	Stain penetration	Darks show
		Opacity	Opaque
	100	Color / oxidation	White (64)

G 297 Opaque Mat

Potash feldspar	42.21	Temperature	C/8-10
Barium carbonate	26.45	Surface @ C/8	Dry mat
E.P. kaolin	12.46	Fluidity	None
Rutile	7.48	Stain penetration	No
Flint	6.60	Opacity	Opaque
Kentucky ball #4	3.13	Color / oxidation	Tan (27)
Zinc oxide	1.51	/ reduction	Gray (93)
Whiting	.16		
	100.00		

G 298 Dry Mat

Kona feldspar	38	Temperature	C/8-10
Flint	36	Surface @ C/8	Dry mat
Whiting	17	Fluidity	None
Talc	6	Stain penetration	No
Zinc oxide	3	Opacity	Opaque
	——	Color / oxidation	White (32)
	100	/ reduction	White (32)

G 299 Cream Mat

Potash feldspar	38.0	Temperature	C/8-10
Whiting	22.0	Surface @ C/8	Dry mat
Kaolin	20.0	Fluidity	Little
Flint	15.9	Stain penetration	Darks show
Titanium oxide	4.1	Opacity	Opaque
	——	Color / oxidation	Cream (63)
	100.0	/ reduction	Tan (40)

G 300 Yellow-ochre

Potash feldspar	35	Temperature	C/8-10
Kaolin	24	Surface @ C/8	Dry mat
Whiting	17	Fluidity	None
Flint	12	Stain penetration	No
Rutile	8	Opacity	Opaque
Spodumene	4	Color / oxidation	Warm yellow-ochre (11)
	——		
	100	/ reduction	Gray-brown (146)

G 301 Tan Mat

Potash feldspar	53.79	Temperature	C/8-10
Whiting	19.21	Surface @ C/8	Dry mat
Kentucky ball #4	19.21	Fluidity	None
Kaolin	4.61	Stain penetration	No
Zinc oxide	3.18	Opacity	Opaque
		Color / oxidation	Tan (152)
	100.00	/ reduction	Grayed pink (47)

G 302 Tan

Potash feldspar	45.9	Temperature	C/8-10
Whiting	22.1	Surface @ C/8	Semimat
E.P. kaolin	12.1	Fluidity	Some
Flint	12.1	Stain penetration	Darks show
Rutile	7.8	Opacity	Opaque
		Color / oxidation	Tan (28)
	100.0	/ reduction	Gray (100)

G 303 OG-22

Soda feldspar	34.36	Temperature	C/8-9
Silica	23.69	Surface @ C/8	Gloss
Colemanite	21.32	Fluidity	Fluid
Whiting	10.66	Stain penetration	Yes
Tin oxide	4.73	Opacity	Transparent
Barium carbonate	3.55	Color / oxidation	Pink areas (45)
Rutile	1.18	/ reduction	Areas of white with
Silicon carbonate	.51		red areas (53)
	100.00		

G 304 Reduction Red

Soda feldspar	31.0	Temperature	C/8
Borax	26.0	Surface @ C/8	Gloss
Flint	19.1	Fluidity	Fluid
China clay	12.5	Stain penetration	Darks show
Whiting	7.0	Opacity	Translucent
Soda ash	2.0	Color / artificial	
Tin oxide	2.0	/ reduction	Black with red areas
Copper carbonate	.4	/ reduction	Brown with red areas
			(155)
	100.0	Note: Broken areas of color (for arti-	
Silicon carbide	.5	ficial reduction)	

G 305 Reduction Purple

Potash feldspar	37.1	Temperature	C/8-10
Flint	27.8	Surface @ C/8	Mat
Whiting	18.6	Fluidity	Some
China clay	9.3	Stain penetration	Yes
Zinc oxide	3.0	Opacity	Translucent
Selenium	2.1	Color / oxidation	Slight white (6)
Cadmium sulfide	2.1	/ reduction	Purple (107)
	100.0		

G 306 Grayed Blue Celadon

Potash feldspar	77.4	Temperature	C/8-9
Flint	13.9	Surface @ C/8	Semigloss
Whiting	5.9	Fluidity	Little
Red iron oxide	2.2	Stain penetration	Darks show
Tin oxide	.6	Opacity	Translucent
		Color / oxidation	White (146)
	100.0	/ reduction	Grayed blue (87)
		Note: Some cracks	

G 307 Blue-green

Potash feldspar	32.1	Temperature	C/8-9
Flint	24.1	Surface @ C/8	Semigloss
Whiting	16.1	Fluidity	Some
Rutile	8.9	Stain penetration	No
Cobalt oxide	8.9	Opacity	Opaque
China clay	8.6	Color / oxidation	Broken blue and
Vanadium pentoxide	1.3		green (91/97)
		/ reduction	Charcoal (145)
	100.0		

G 308 Oxidation Light Blue

Soda feldspar	25.5	Temperature	C/8-10
Boric acid	24.1	Surface @ C/8	Gloss
Flint	12.2	Fluidity	Fluid
Soda ash	9.9	Stain penetration	Yes
Soda bicarbonate	9.9	Opacity	Translucent
Kaolin	9.5	Color / oxidation	Light blue (86)
Whiting	5.7	/ reduction	Broken white, brown,
Tin oxide	2.9		red, and black
Copper carbonate	.3		
	100.0		

G 309 Dark Olive

Nepheline syenite	33.5	Temperature	C/8-10
Silica	28.6	Surface @ C/8	Semigloss
Whiting	16.1	Fluidity	Some
Red iron oxide	12.3	Stain penetration	No
Kaolin	8.0	Opacity	Opaque
Bentonite	1.0	Color / oxidation	Dark olive (137)
Calcium	.5	/ reduction	Metallic brown-black
	100.0		

G 310 Dark Green

Potash feldspar	32.7	Temperature	C/8-9
Flint	24.5	Surface @ C/8	Semimat
Whiting	16.4	Fluidity	Some
Rutile	9.1	Stain penetration	No
China clay	8.2	Opacity	Opaque
Copper oxide	7.3	Color / oxidation	Dark green (129)
Molybdenum	1.8	/ reduction	Dark gray-green (dark 139)
	100.0		

G 311 Oxidation Green

Flint	32.0	Temperature	**C/8**
Cornwall stone	27.0	Surface @ C/8	Gloss
Borax	21.0	Fluidity	Very fluid
Barium carbonate	9.0	Stain penetration	Yes
Soda ash	4.5	Opacity	Transparent
Zinc oxide	4.0	Color / oxidation	Medium green (130)
Copper carbonate	2.0	/ reduction	Red with green areas (52)
Tin oxide	2.0		
	101.5		

G 312 Temmoku

Stoneware clay	24	Temperature	C/8-10
Flint	24	Surface @ C/8	Semigloss
Potash feldspar	22	Fluidity	Little
Whiting	18	Stain penetration	No
Red iron oxide	9	Opacity	Opaque
Spodumene	3	Color / oxidation	Dark olive (137)
	100	/ reduction	Black (113)

G 313 K.C.N.S. Brown

Potash feldspar	56.5	Temperature	C/8-10
Flint	23.0	Surface @ C/8	Semigloss
Red iron oxide	9.0	Fluidity	None
Whiting	7.0	Stain penetration	No
Kaolin	4.5	Opacity	Opaque
	———	Color / oxidation	Brown (155)
	100.0		

G 314 Reduction Dark Brown

Potash feldspar	51	Temperature	C/8-10
Kaolin	18	Surface @ C/8	Mat
Flint	14	Fluidity	None
Red iron oxide	11	Stain penetration	No
Whiting	6	Opacity	Opaque
	———	Color / oxidation	Dark brown (73)
	100	/ reduction	Dark brown, metallic (73)

G 315 Oxidation Red-brown

Hardwood ash	45	Temperature	C/8-10
Yellow ochre	45	Surface @ C/8	Dry mat
Whiting	10	Fluidity	None
	———	Stain penetration	No
	100	Opacity	Opaque
		Color / oxidation	Red-brown (73)
		/ reduction	Metallic black (145)

G 316 Mat Brown

Potash feldspar	50.0	Temperature	C/8-10
Flint	18.6	Surface @ C/8	Mat
Kaolin	17.1	Fluidity	None
Red iron oxide	9.2	Stain penetration	No
Whiting	5.1	Opacity	Opaque
	———	Color / oxidation	Dark brown (73)
	100.0	/ reduction	Brown, metallic (49)

G 317 Gloss/Mat Brown

Potash feldspar	40	Temperature	C/8-9
Whiting	28	Surface @ C/8	Gloss/mat
Ilmenite	12	Fluidity	Some
Manganese dioxide	8	Stain penetration	No
Flint	4	Opacity	Opaque
Red iron oxide	4	Color / oxidation	Dark brown (dark
Red clay	4		155), aventurine with specks
	——	/ reduction	Dark brown (dark 75)
	100		

G 318 Brown

Potash feldspar	31.3	Temperature	C/8-9
Flint	23.6	Surface @ C/8	Semigloss
Whiting	15.7	Fluidity	Some
Manganese dioxide	11.3	Stain penetration	None
Rutile	8.7	Opacity	Opaque
China clay	7.8	Color / oxidation	Brown (156)
Vanadium	1.6	/reduction	Brown (154)
	——		
	100.0		

G 319 Gloss Brown

Flint	30	Temperature	C/8-9
Potash feldspar	30	Surface @ C/8	Gloss
Whiting	18	Fluidity	Some
China clay	8	Stain penetration	Darks show
Volcanic ash	6	Opacity	Opaque
Burnt sienna	4	Color / oxidation	Dark brown (dark
Kentucky ball #4	3		147)
Red iron oxide	1	/ reduction	Black (113)
	——		
	100		

G 320 Reduction Charcoal

Stoneware clay	24	Temperature	C/8-9
Flint	24	Surface @ C/8	Semigloss
Potash feldspar	21	Fluidity	Some
Whiting	16	Stain penetration	No
Red iron oxide	11	Opacity	Opaque
Spodumene	4	Color / oxidation	Dark olive (137)
	___	/ reduction	Charcoal (145)
	100		

G 321 Reduction Black

Potash feldspar	66.12	Temperature	C/8-9
Whiting	8.26	Surface @ C/8	Gloss
Flint	8.26	Fluidity	Some
Tin oxide	8.26	Stain penetration	None
Red iron oxide	5.79	Opacity	Opaque
Zinc oxide	3.31	Color / oxidation	Tan (37)
154)	___	/ reduction	Brown-black (113/
	100.00		154)

G 322 Reduction Semigloss Black

Potash feldspar	43	Temperature	C/8
Silica	20	Surface @ C/8	Semigloss
Whiting	14	Fluidity	Fluid
China clay	12	Stain penetration	None
Black iron oxide	9	Opacity	Opaque
Zinc oxide	2	Color / oxidation	Dark olive (dark 137)
	___	/ reduction	Black (113)
	100		

G 323 Reduction Gray

Potash feldspar	32.24	Temperature	C/8
Flint	25.37	Surface @ C/8	Semigloss
Whiting	9.86	Fluidity	Some
Barium carbonate	8.31	Stain penetration	Very darks show
Rutile	6.20	Opacity	Opaque
Tin oxide	5.64	Color / oxidation	Grayed pink (44)
Zinc oxide	4.23	/ reduction	Gray (103)
Kaolin	3.64		
Colemanite	3.58		
Fluorspar	.65		
Cobalt carbonate	.28		
	100.00		

CONE/9

G 324 Clear Gloss

Cornwall stone	82	Temperature	C/9-10
Whiting	14	Surface @ C/9	Gloss
Nepheline syenite	4	Fluidity	Some
	———	Stain penetration	Yes
	100	Opacity	Transparent
		Color / oxidation	Clear
		/ reduction	Clear

G 325 Gloss

Kona feldspar	79	Temperature	C/9-10
Whiting	12	Surface @ C/9	Gloss
Zinc oxide	6	Fluidity	Some
Spodumene	3	Stain penetration	Yes
	———	Opacity	Transparent
	100	Color / oxidation	Clear
		/ reduction	Clear

G 326 Transparent Gloss

Nepheline syenite	53	Temperature	C/9
Flint	28	Surface @ C/9	Gloss
Whiting	10	Fluidity	Fluid
Dolomite	5	Stain penetration	Yes
Colemanite	4	Opacity	Transparent
	———	Color / oxidation	Clear
	100	/ reduction	Clear

G 327 Soda Feldspar Gloss

Soda feldspar	47.8	Temperature	C/9
Silica	27.4	Surface @ C/9	Gloss
Colemite	11.8	Fluidity	Fluid
Barium carbonate	6.5	Stain penetration	Yes
Whiting	3.9	Opacity	Transparent
Zinc oxide	2.6	Color / oxidation	Clear
		/ reduction	Clear
	100.0		

G 328 Little Flow Gloss

Potash feldspar	47.6	Temperature	C/9-10
Flint	19.0	Surface @ C/9	Gloss
Whiting	14.3	Fluidity	Some
Kaolin	14.3	Stain penetration	Yes
Spodumene	4.8	Opacity	Transparent
		Color / oxidation	Clear
	100.0	/ reduction	Clear
		Note: Cracks	

G 329 Kona Feldspar Gloss

Kona feldspar	46.3	Temperature	C/9-10
Flint	29.0	Surface @ C/9	Gloss
Whiting	10.0	Fluidity	Some
Dolomite	6.1	Stain penetration	Yes
Zinc oxide	5.7	Opacity	Transparent
China clay	1.6	Color / oxidation	Clear
Spodumene	1.3	/ reduction	Clear
		Note: Some cracks	
	100.0		

G 330 Transparent

Potash feldspar	42	Temperature	C/9
Flint	27	Surface @ C/9	Gloss
Whiting	17	Fluidity	Some
Kaolin	13	Stain penetration	Yes
Zinc oxide	1	Opacity	Transparent
	_____	Color / oxidation	Clear
	100	/ reduction	Clear

G 331 Clear

Potash feldspar	40	Temperature	C/9
Whiting	20	Surface @ C/9	Gloss
Cornwall stone	20	Fluidity	Fluid
Barium carbonate	20	Stain penetration	Yes
	_____	Opacity	Transparent
	100	Color / oxidation	Clear
		/ reduction	Clear

G 332 Gloss with Cracks

Kona feldspar	39	Temperature	C/9
Flint	26	Surface @ C/9	Gloss
Whiting	12	Fluidity	Some
Barium carbonate	8	Stain penetration	Yes
Colemanite	7	Opacity	Transparent
Kaolin	4	Color / oxidation	Clear
Magnesium carbonate	3	/ reduction	Clear
Zinc oxide	1	Note: Some cracks	
	_____		
	100		

G 333 Translucent

Potash feldspar	82.9	Temperature	C/9-10
Whiting	9.0	Surface @ C/9	Gloss
Flint	8.1	Fluidity	Little
	———	Stain penetration	Yes
	100.0	Opacity	Translucent
		Color / oxidation	White (32)
		/ reduction	Clear

G 334 Translucent Gloss

Cornwall stone	40	Temperature	C/9-10
Flint	26	Surface @ C/9	Gloss
Kaolin	15	Fluidity	Some
Whiting	10	Stain penetration	Darks show
Dolomite	4	Opacity	Translucent
Colemanite	3	Color / oxidation	Off-white (30)
Zinc oxide	2	/ reduction	Off-white (8)
	———		
	100		

G 335 Potash Feldspar Translucent

Potash feldspar	35.4	Temperature	C/9-10
Spodumene	19.1	Surface @ C/9	Gloss
Flint	17.3	Fluidity	Fluid
Colemanite	10.5	Stain penetration	Yes
Talc	10.1	Opacity	Translucent
Zircopax	4.0	Color / oxidation	Slight white (6)
Boric acid	3.6	/ reduction	Slight gray (8)
	———		
	100.0		

G 336 Bains's Semigloss

Potash feldspar	46.20	Temperature	C/9-10
Barium carbonate	15.45	Surface @ C/9	Semigloss
Kentucky ball #4	9.20	Fluidity	Fluid
Flint	6.71	Stain penetration	Darks show
Whiting	6.52	Opacity	Translucent
Zinc oxide	5.91	Color / oxidation	White (7)
Talc	3.64	/ reduction	White (8)
Colemanite	2.99		
Dolomite	1.91		
Rutile	.47		
	99.00		

G 337 Semigloss Translucent (Boling D-12)

Nepheline syenite	45	Temperature	C/9
Flint	29	Surface @ C/9	Semigloss
Dolomite	10	Fluidity	Fluid
Whiting	8	Stain penetration	Darks show
Talc	7	Opacity	Translucent, thin
Bentonite	3		Opaque, thick
Red iron oxide	3	Color / oxidation	Grayed tan (150)
Rutile	1	/ reduction	Brown (157)
	106		

G 338 Driscoll's Semigloss

Flint	36.65	Temperature	C/9-10
Kona feldspar	18.23	Surface @ C/9	Semigloss
China clay	16.92	Fluidity	None
Zinc oxide	16.92	Stain penetration	Darks show
Whiting	11.28	Opacity	Translucent
		Color / oxidation	Some white (31)
	100.00	/ reduction	Some gray (8)

G 339 White Semigloss

Nepheline syenite	31.9	Temperature	C/9-10
Flint	30.9	Surface @ C/9	Semigloss
Whiting	19.0	Fluidity	Some
Kaolin	13.2	Stain penetration	Yes
Tin oxide	5.0	Opacity	Translucent
		Color / oxidation	White (7)
	100.0	/ reduction	Clear

G 340 RG Semimat

Nepheline syenite	70.42	Temperature	C/9-10
Silica	8.42	Surface @ C/9	Semimat
E.P. kaolin	7.02	Fluidity	Some
Dolomite	4.69	Stain penetration	Darks show
Barium carbonate	4.21	Opacity	Translucent
Whiting	2.81	Color / oxidation	Off-white (31)
Zinc oxide	2.11	/ reduction	White (7)
	99.68		

G 341 Chun

Potash feldspar	42.1	Temperature	C/9-10
Flint	27.2	Surface @ C/9	Semimat
Colemanite	8.8	Fluidity	Fluid
Dolomite	8.8	Stain penetration	Darks show
Barium carbonate	4.4	Opacity	Translucent
Tin oxide	2.6	Color / oxidation	White (32)
Whiting	2.6		
Kaolin	1.8		
Zinc oxide	1.7		
	100.0		

G 342 Translucent Semimat

Potash feldspar	40	Temperature	C/9-10
Whiting	20	Surface @ C/9	Semimat
Cornwall stone	20	Fluidity	Some
Kentucky ball #4	20	Stain penetration	Darks show
	___	Opacity	Translucent
	100	Color / oxidation	Off-white (15)
		/ reduction	Gray (8)

G 343 Semimat #33

Kingman feldspar	35	Temperature	C/9-10
E.P. kaolin	23	Surface @ C/9	Semimat
Dolomite	20	Fluidity	Some
Flint	19	Stain penetration	Darks show
Whiting	3	Opacity	Translucent
	___	Color / oxidation	White (6)
	100	/ reduction	Off-white (7)

G 344 Cornwall Mat

Cornwall stone	60	Temperature	C/9-10
Whiting	40	Surface @ C/9	Mat
	___	Fluidity	Some
	100	Stain penetration	Darks show
		Opacity	Translucent
		Color / oxidation	White (6)
		/ reduction	Gray (8)

G 345 Synthetic Ash (Sue Cahill, University of Illinois, Urbana, Illinois)

Nepheline syenite	50	Temperature	C/9
Whiting	50	Surface @ C/9	Mat
	___	Fluidity	Fluid
	100	Stain penetration	Darks show
		Opacity	Translucent
		Color / oxidation	White (31)
		/ reduction	Gray (104)

G 346 Translucent Mat

Kona feldspar	35	Temperature	C/9
Hardwood ash	28	Surface @ C/9	Mat
China clay	15	Fluidity	Fluid
Talc	15	Stain penetration	Darks show
Volcanic ash	6	Opacity	Translucent
Tin oxide	1	Color / oxidation	Tan (27)
	——	/ reduction	Off-white (152)
	100	Note: Dark green in recessed areas	

G 347 Opaque Mat

Nepheline syenite	61.4	Temperature	C/9-11
Spodumene	13.2	Surface @ C/9	Mat
Silica	8.7	Fluidity	Little
Kaolin	6.9	Stain penetration	Darks show
Dolomite	4.9	Opacity	Opaque
Whiting	2.7	Color / oxidation	White (6)
Zinc oxide	2.2	/ reduction	Gray (104)
	100.0		

G 348 Off-white Mat

Potash feldspar	50.7	Temperature	C/9-10
Kaolin	28.1	Surface @ C/9	Mat
Whiting	21.2	Fluidity	Some
	——	Stain penetration	Darks show
	100.0	Opacity	Opaque
		Color / oxidation	Off-white (15)
		/ reduction	Off-white (7)

G 349 Opaque Mat

Kona feldspar	48	Temperature	C/9-10
China clay	25	Surface @ C/9	Mat
Dolomite	22	Fluidity	Some
Whiting	5	Stain penetration	None
	‾‾‾	Opacity	Opaque
	100	Color / oxidation	White (7)
		/ reduction	Off-white (8)

G 350 Roy's Spotted Mat

Potash feldspar	45.34	Temperature	C/9-10
Barium carbonate	18.22	Surface @ C/9	Mat
Kentucky ball #4	8.67	Fluidity	Fluid
Whiting	7.68	Stain penetration	Darks show
Rutile	7.51	Opacity	Opaque
Zinc oxide	6.69	Color / oxidation	Broken white-tan
Bone ash	4.62		(6-29)
Titanium dioxide	1.00	/ reduction	Broken white-gray
	‾‾‾		(7-8)
	99.73		

G 351 MG 2

Potash feldspar	41.65	Temperature	C/9-10
Flint	19.89	Surface @ C/9	Mat
Talc	14.59	Fluidity	Some
Colemanite	11.94	Stain penetration	Darks show
Dolomite	7.62	Opacity	Opaque
Kaolin	4.31	Color / oxidation	White (32)
	‾‾‾	/ reduction	White (7)
	100.00		

G 352 Mat

Potash feldspar	41.1	Temperature	C/9-10
Kaolin	21.8	Surface @ C/9	Mat
Whiting	17.5	Fluidity	Some
Flint	10.5	Stain penetration	Very darks show
Zinc oxide	4.5	Opacity	Opaque
Rutile	2.7	Color / oxidation	Broken cream (30)
Tin oxide	1.9	/ reduction	Broken gray-pink
			(8-47)
	100.0		

G 353 White Mat 4321

Potash feldspar	40	Temperature	C/9-10
Dolomite	30	Surface @ C/9	Mat
Colemanite	20	Fluidity	Fluid
Kaolin	10	Stain penetration	Darks show
		Opacity	Opaque
	100	Color / oxidation	Broken white (31)
		/ reduction	Gray (104)

G 354 Opaque Mat

Nepheline syenite	32.0	Temperature	C/9
Kaolin	21.4	Surface @ C/9	Mat
Flint	17.3	Fluidity	Fluid
Dolomite	13.2	Stain penetration	Darks show
Whiting	7.5	Opacity	Opaque
Zinc oxide	6.0	Color / oxidation	White (6)
Spodumene	2.6	/ reduction	Gray (8)
	100.0		

G 355 White

Potash feldspar	33	Temperature	C/9-10
Dolomite	23	Surface @ C/9	Mat
Kaolin	22	Fluidity	Some
Flint	22	Stain penetration	Darks show
	——	Opacity	Opaque
	100	Color / oxidation	White (6)
		/ reduction	Gray (8)

G 356 Smith's Spodumene

Soda feldspar	29.44	Temperature	C/9-11
Kaolin	22.08	Surface @ C/9	Smooth mat
Dolomite	21.98	Fluidity	Some
Spodumene	19.63	Stain penetration	Darks show
Whiting	6.87	Opacity	Opaque
	———	Color / oxidation	White (32)
	100.00	/ reduction	Gray (8)

G 357 White Mat

Kaolin	33	Temperature	C/9-11
Dolomite	30	Surface @ C/9	Mat
Potash feldspar	25	Fluidity	Little
Flint	7	Opacity	Opaque
Whiting	5	Stain penetration	Very darks show
	——	Color / oxidation	White (32)
	100	/ reduction	Gray (8)

G 358 Kona Feldspar Mat

Kona feldspar	25.0	Temperature	C/9-10
Whiting	21.0	Surface @ C/9	Mat
Volcanic ash	19.3	Fluidity	Little
Titanium dioxide	10.0	Stain penetration	None
Kaolin	11.3	Opacity	Opaque
Flint	11.2	Color / oxidation	Tan (30)
Zinc oxide	2.2	/ reduction	Off-white (31)
	100.0		

G 359 Buff Gloss

Kona feldspar	35	Temperature	C/9
Flint	20	Surface @ C/9	Gloss
Dolomite	15	Fluidity	Fluid
Kaolin	10	Stain penetration	Yes
Volcanic ash	10	Opacity	Transparent
Hardwood ash	10	Color / oxidation	Buff (15)
Rutile	1	/ reduction	Clear with green in recessed areas
	101		

G 360 Opalescence

Nephaline syenite	63.9	Temperature	C/9
Frit #25	12.8	Surface @ C/9	Gloss
Vanadium pentoxide	6.8	Fluidity	Very fluid
Whiting	6.4	Stain penetration	Yes
China clay	3.7	Opacity / oxidation	Transparent
Lithium carbonate	2.7	Color / oxidation	Opalescence where thick
Zinc oxide	1.9		
Flint	1.8	Opacity / reduction	Opaque
	100.0	Color / reduction	Broken black, white, and blue

G 361 Off-red

Soda feldspar	53.0	Temperature	C/9
Flint	17.0	Surface @ C/9	Gloss
Whiting	15.0	Fluidity	Some
Kaolin	6.0	Stain penetration	Yes
Zinc oxide	5.0	Opacity	Transparent
Talc	4.0	Color / oxidation	Light blue-green
Tin oxide	1.0		(light 84)
Copper oxide	.5	/ reduction	Off-red (78)
	101.5		

G 362 Rust Reduction

Potash feldspar	47.9	Temperature	C/9-10
Whiting	20.0	Surface @ C/9	Mat
Calcined kaolin	14.3	Fluidity	Some
Kaolin	12.3	Stain penetration	None
Red iron oxide	3.2	Opacity	Opaque
Zinc oxide	1.7	Color / oxidation	Rust (33)
Chromium oxide	.6	/ reduction	Charcoal (115)
	100.0		

G 363 Red Reduction

Soda feldspar	43.6	Temperature	C/9
Flint	26.0	Surface @ C/9	Gloss
Whiting	13.6	Fluidity	Fluid
Frit #399	13.0	Stain penetration	Yes
E. P. kaolin	2.3	Opacity / oxidation	Transparent
Tin oxide	1.1	Color / oxidation	Pale blue (86)
Copper carbonate	.4	Opacity / reduction	Opaque
		Color / reduction	Red (50)
	100.0		

G 364 Peach Blossom

Flint	41.7	Temperature	C/9
Nepheline syenite	27.6	Surface @ C/9	Gloss
Colemanite	17.1	Fluidity	Fluid
Dolomite	12.7	Stain penetration	Darks show
Copper carbonate	.3	Opacity	Translucent
Yellow ochre	.3	Color / oxidation	Broken blue (86)
Tin oxide	.3	/ reduction	Broken red,
			magenta, green,
	100.0		and brown

G 365 Reduction Red-pink

Flint	36.4	Temperature	C/9
Potash feldspar	34.0	Surface @ C/9	Gloss
Whiting	15.6	Fluidity	Very fluid
Calcined borax	11.0	Stain penetration	Yes
Tin oxide	1.7	Opacity / oxidation	Transparent
China clay	.8	Color / oxidation	Blue where thick (87)
Copper carbonate	.5	Opacity / reduction	Opaque
		Color / reduction	Red-pink (51-52)
	100.0		

G 366 Blue

Potash feldspar	38.8	Temperature	C/9-10
Flint	29.2	Surface @ C/9	Mat
Whiting	19.4	Fluidity	Some
China clay	7.7	Stain penetration	None
Barnard clay	1.9	Opacity	Opaque
Tin oxide	1.9	Color / oxidation	Blue (89)
Red clay	.5	/ reduction	Blue (90)
Red iron oxide	.3		
Cobalt oxide	.3		
	100.0		

G 367 Semimat Blue

Potash feldspar	38.0	Temperature	C/9
Whiting	21.0	Surface @ C/9	Semimat
Kaolin	20.2	Fluidity	Fluid
Flint	15.2	Stain penetration	None
Titanium dioxide	4.1	Opacity	Opaque
Cobalt carbonate	1.5	Color / oxidation	Blue (92)
	———	/ reduction	Blue (93)
	100.0		

G 368 Green

Kona feldspar	42.6	Temperature	C/9
Whiting	17.2	Surface @ C/9	Gloss
Kaolin	17.0	Fluidity	Fluid
Flint	9.1	Stain penetration	Yes
Colemanite	8.1	Opacity	Transparent
Barium carbonate	5.8	Color / oxidation	Light green (144)
Chromium oxide	.2	/ reduction	Green in recessed
	———		areas (130)
	100.0		

G 369 Tan Mat

Potash feldspar	44	Temperature	C/9
Whiting	22	Surface @ C/9	Mat
Flint	12	Fluidity	Fluid
Kaolin	11	Stain penetration	None
Rutile	8	Opacity	Opaque
Iron oxide	3	Color / oxidation	Broken tan-rust
Zinc oxide	1		(27-34)
	———	/ reduction	Tan (28-158)
	101		

G 370 Tan Opaque (Ron Carlson, San Diego State University, San Diego, California)

Albany slip	30	Temperature	C/9
Nepheline syenite	30	Surface @ C/9	Mat
Whiting	15	Fluidity	Some
Rutile	10	Stain penetration	Darks show
Flint	10	Opacity	Opaque
Barium	5	Color / oxidation	Tan (18)
		/ reduction	Brown (33)
	100		

G 371 Shanner's Brown

Potash feldspar	45.35	Temperature	C/9
Kaolin	21.51	Surface @ C/9	Mat
Whiting	20.91	Fluidity	Fluid
Red iron oxide	7.07	Stain penetration	None
Talc	3.44	Opacity	Opaque
Bone ash	1.72	Color / oxidation	Yellow-brown (17)
		/ reduction	Brown (159-153)
	100.00		

G 372 Gloss Brown

Flint	36.67	Temperature	C/9
Potash feldspar	30.03	Surface @ C/9	Gloss
Whiting	13.37	Fluidity	Fluid
Kaolin	11.52	Stain penetration	None
Red iron oxide	4.21	Opacity	Opaque
Rutile	4.20	Color / oxidation	Brown (73)
		/ reduction	Broken brown-gray
	100.00		(33-100)

G 373 Reduction Black

Potash feldspar	42.0	Temperature	C/9
Flint	21.1	Surface @ C/9	Gloss
Whiting	15.8	Fluidity	Fluid
Kaolin	9.9	Stain penetration	None
Red iron oxide	9.1	Opacity	Opaque
Zinc oxide	2.1	Color / oxidation	Brown-black (113-73)
	———	/ reduction	Black (113)
	100.0		

G 374 Gloss Black

Potash feldspar	33.6	Temperature	C/9
Flint	24.5	Surface @ C/9	Gloss
Whiting	15.8	Fluidity	Some
Kaolin	11.8	Stain penetration	None
Black iron oxide	10.1	Opacity	Opaque
Volcanic ash	4.1	Color / oxidation	Black (113)
	———	/ reduction	Black (113)
	99.9		

CONE/10

G 375 Moonlight

Cornwall stone	63.8	Temperature	C/10
Colemanite	14.3	Surface @ C/10	Gloss
Flint	7.6	Fluidity	Fluid
Whiting	7.6	Stain penetration	Yes
E.P. kaolin	4.8	Opacity	Transparent
Zinc oxide	1.9	Color / oxidation	Clear
	———	/ reduction	Clear
	100.0		
Rutile	3.2⎰	Color / oxidation	Opalescence in thick
Ilmenite	2.0⎱		areas
		/ reduction	Broken white, tan, and blue

G 376 Gloss

Nepheline syenite	55.5	Temperature	C/10-11
Potash feldspar	23.8	Surface @ C/10	Gloss
Talc	17.4	Fluidity	Little
Bentonite	2.4	Stain penetration	Yes
Zinc oxide	.9	Opacity	Transparent, thin
	———	Color / oxidation	Clear
	100.0	/ reduction	Clear
		Note: Some white where thick	

G 377 Reduction Gloss

Nepheline syenite	54.65	Temperature	C/10
Flint	23.39	Surface @ C/10	Gloss
Colemanite	9.75	Fluidity	Fluid
Cryolite	6.46	Stain penetration	Yes
Lithium carbonate	3.96	Opacity	Transparent
Barium carbonate	1.39	Color / oxidation	Clear
gray	———	/ reduction	Clear with broken
	99.60		gray areas

G 378 Secrest

Potash feldspar	53.0	Temperature	C/10-11
Flint	24.0	Surface @ C/10	Gloss
Whiting	12.0	Fluidity	Little
Kaolin	6.0	Stain penetration	Yes
Zinc oxide	2.5	Opacity	Transparent
Barium carbonate	2.5	Color / oxidation	Clear
	———	/ reduction	Clear
	100.0		

G 379 Clear Gloss

Kona feldspar	50.0	Temperature	C/10
Flint	24.9	Surface @ C/10	Gloss
Whiting	17.0	Fluidity	Fluid
Kaolin	3.7	Stain penetration	Yes
Dolomite	2.5	Opacity	Transparent
Zinc oxide	1.0	Color / oxidation	Clear
Spodumene	.9	/ reduction	Clear
	———	Note: Some white where thick	
	100.0		

G 380 Transparent

Potash feldspar	49.5	Temperature	C/10
Spodumene	19.7	Surface @ C/10	Gloss
Talc	11.8	Fluidity	Fluid
Kentucky ball #4	9.9	Stain penetration	Yes
Whiting	5.0	Opacity	Transparent
Lead bisilicate	3.0	Color / oxidation	Clear
Zinc oxide	1.1	/ reduction	Clear
	———	Note: Some cracks	
	100.0		

G 381 Clear

Cornwall stone	46.82	Temperature	C/10-11
Silica	19.54	Surface @ C/10	Gloss
Kaolin	15.11	Fluidity	Little
Whiting	12.55	Stain penetration	Yes
Dolomite	4.89	Opacity	Transparent
Zinc oxide	1.09	Color / oxidation	Clear
	——	/ reduction	Clear
	100.00	Note: Some white where thick	

G 382 Clear Gloss

Potash feldspar	40	Temperature	C/10-11
Nepheline syenite	35	Surface @ C/10	Gloss
Talc	15	Fluidity	None
Kentucky ball #4	5	Stain penetration	Yes
Spodumene	5	Opacity	Transparent
	——	Color / oxidation	Clear
	100	/ reduction	Clear

G 383 Gloss N

Soda feldspar	37.38	Temperature	C/10
Flint	24.27	Surface @ C/10	Gloss
Colemanite	22.86	Fluidity	Fluid
Whiting	11.12	Stain penetration	Yes
Barium carbonate	3.87	Opacity	Transparent, thin
	——	Color / oxidation	Clear
	99.50	/ reduction	Clear
		Note: Opalescent white where thick	

G 384 Autumn

Potash feldspar	26	Temperature	C/10
Lincoln clay	26	Surface @ C/10	Gloss
Whiting	25	Fluidity	Some
Silica	22	Stain penetration	Yes
	___	Opacity	Transparent
	99	Color / oxidation	Clear
		/ reduction	Clear, slight green where thick

G 385 Otis #3 Barium

Soda feldspar	91.7	Temperature	C/10
Barium carbonate	4.0	Surface @ C/10	Gloss
Bentonite	2.3	Fluidity	Little
Whiting	2.0	Stain penetration	Darks show
	___	Opacity	Translucent
	100.0	Color / oxidation	White (7)
		/ reduction	Gray (8)

G 386 Gloss K2

Potash feldspar	57.77	Temperature	C/10
Kentucky ball #4	12.92	Surface @ C/10	Gloss
Dolomite	9.56	Fluidity	Fluid
Whiting	7.75	Stain penetration	Yes
E.P. kaolin	5.42	Opacity	Translucent
Barium carbonate	5.16	Color / oxidation	Slight white (32)
Opax	1.41	/ reduction	Clear with cracks
	___		
	99.99		

G 387 Translucent Gloss

Potash feldspar	55.8	Temperature	C/10
E.P. kaolin	18.6	Surface @ C/10	Gloss
Whiting	18.6	Fluidity	Some
Flint	4.7	Stain penetration	Yes
Tin oxide	2.3	Opacity	Translucent
	———	Color / oxidation	White (7)
	100.0	/ reduction	Gray (104)

G 388 White Gloss

Cornwall stone	46.5	Temperature	C/10
Colemanite	27.9	Surface @ C/10	Gloss
Silica	18.6	Fluidity	Some
Whiting	7.0	Stain penetration	Yes
	———	Opacity	Translucent
	100.0	Color / oxidation	White (32)
		/ reduction	Buff (29)
Red iron oxide	2.0	Color / oxidation	Buff (30)
		/ reduction	Broken white and grays

G 389 Gloss

Potash feldspar	39.0	Temperature	C/10-11
Flint	22.2	Surface @ C/10	Gloss
Whiting	19.0	Fluidity	Little
Kentucky ball #4	13.8	Stain penetration	Yes
Spodumene	6.0	Opacity	Translucent
	———	Color / oxidation	Slight white where thick
	100.0		
		/ reduction	Slight white where thick

G 390 Gloss

Flint	31.9	Temperature	C/10-11
Potash feldspar	31.7	Surface C/10	Gloss
Whiting	18.7	Fluidity	Little
Kaolin	14.8	Stain penetration	Yes
Spodumene	2.4	Opacity	Translucent, thick
Zinc oxide	.5	Color / oxidation	Some white
		/ reduction	Some white
	100.0		

G 391 Soda Feldspar Gloss

Soda feldspar	30.9	Temperature	C/10-11
Flint	25.4	Surface @ C/10	Gloss
Zinc oxide	16.7	Fluidity	Some
Kaolin	11.9	Stain penetration	Yes
Whiting	9.7	Opacity	Translucent, thick
Spodumene	5.4	Color / oxidation	Some white
		/ reduction	Some white
	100.0	Stain penetration	Darks show
Copper carbonate	2.0	Opacity	Translucent
		Color / oxidation	Green (139)
		/ reduction	Gray-pink(107)

G 392 White Gloss

Soda feldspar	30.1	Temperature	C/10
Flint	29.1	Surface @ C/10	Gloss
Whiting	25.2	Fluidity	Some
Kaolin	15.6	Stain penetration	Yes
		Opacity	Translucent
	100.0	Color / oxidation	White (32)
		/ reduction	White (32)

G 393 Translucent

Zinc oxide	28	Temperature	C/10-11
Potash feldspar	23	Surface @ C/10	Gloss
Soda feldspar	23	Fluidity	Some
Flint	13	Stain penetration	Darks show
Whiting	9	Opacity	Translucent
Rutile	4	Color / oxidation	White (32)
	———	/ reduction	Brown (155)
	100		

G 394 Marshmallow

Potash feldspar	33.99	Temperature	C/10
Flint	22.18	Surface @ C/10	Gloss
Zircopax	12.52	Fluidity	Some
Colemanite	11.09	Stain penetration	Darks show
Whiting	6.71	Opacity	Opaque
Talc	5.01	Color / oxidation	White (32)
Zinc oxide	4.29	/ reduction	White (7)
Kaolin	4.20		
	———		
	99.99		

G 395 Semigloss

Potash feldspar	30	Temperature	C/10
Flint	29	Surface @ C/10	Semigloss
Whiting	24	Fluidity	Some
Kaolin	12	Stain penetration	Yes
Spodumene	5	Opacity	Transparent
	———	Color / oxidation	Clear
	100	/ reduction	Clear

G 396 Clear Semigloss

Potash feldspar	30.5	Temperature	C/10
Flint	29.6	Surface @ C/10	Semigloss
Whiting	18.5	Fluidity	Some
E.P. kaolin	13.8	Stain penetration	Yes
Zinc oxide	7.6	Opacity	Transparent
		Color / oxidation	Clear
	100.0	/ reduction	Clear

Note: Some white where thick

G 397 Cream Semigloss (W. Chapman, Mesa College, San Diego, California)

Potash feldspar	40	Temperature	C/10
Whiting	20	Surface @ C/10	Semigloss
Cornwall stone	20	Fluidity	Some
Kentucky ball #4	20	Stain penetration	Yes
		Opacity	Translucent
	100	Color / oxidation	Cream (15)
		/ reduction	White (7)

G 398 Driscoll's Zinc

Flint	36.55	Temperature	C/10-11
Kingman feldspar	18.36	Surface @ C/10	Semigloss
Zinc oxide	17.01	Fluidity	None
China clay	16.74	Stain penetration	Darks show
Whiting	11.34	Opacity	Translucent
		Color / oxidation	White (32)
	100.00	/ reduction	Off-white (8)

G 399 Translucent Semigloss (Alfred University, Alfred, New York)

Flint	32.69	Temperature	C/10-12
Buckingspar	27.04	Surface @ C/10	Semigloss
E.P. kaolin	19.82	Fluidity	Little
Whiting	19.46	Stain penetration	Yes
Red iron oxide	1.09	Opacity	Translucent
	———	Color / oxidation	Off-white (5)
	100.10	/ reduction	Gray (135)

G 400 Opaque Semigloss

Potash feldspar	78.0	Temperature	C/10-12
Whiting	17.3	Surface @ C/10	Semigloss
Bentonite	2.4	Fluidity	None
Zinc oxide	2.3	Stain penetration	None
	———	Opacity	Opaque
	100.0	Color / oxidation	White (32)
		/ reduction	White (7)

G 401 Opaque

Potash feldspar	67.9	Temperature	C/10-11
Flint	12.0	Surface @ C/10	Semigloss
Whiting	11.4	Fluidity	Little
Kaolin	6.3	Stain penetration	Darks show
Zinc oxide	2.4	Opacity	Opaque
	———	Color / oxidation	White (7)
	100.0	/ reduction	Gray (8)
		Note: Cracks	

G 402 Opaque White

Potash feldspar	48	Temperature	C/10-11
Flint	30	Surface @ C/10	Semigloss
Dolomite	10	Fluidity	Little
Colemanite	5	Stain penetration	Darks show
Whiting	3	Opacity	Opaque
China clay	2	Color / oxidation	White (32)
Zinc oxide	2	/ reduction	White (7)
	100		

G 403 Fluid Semigloss

Cornwall stone	43.86	Temperature	C/10
Colemanite	43.86	Surface @ C/10	Semigloss
Rutile	9.50	Fluidity	Very fluid
Red iron oxide	1.39	Stain penetration	Darks show
Alumina oxide	1.39	Opacity	Opaque
		Color / oxidation	Broken white-tan (30-21)
	100.00	/ reduction	Brown (35-27)

G 404 Semigloss

Zinc oxide	43.53	Temperature	C/10-12
Potash feldspar	23.96	Surface @ C/10	Semigloss
Flint	18.03	Fluidity	None
Whiting	13.91	Stain penetration	Darks show
Rutile	.57	Opacity	Opaque
		Color / oxidation	White (6)
	100.00	/ reduction	Off-white (8)

G 405 White

Potash feldspar	40.8	Temperature	C/10
Flint	19.7	Surface @ C/10	Semigloss
Talc	13.9	Fluidity	Fluid
Colemanite	11.9	Stain penetration	Darks show
Dolomite	6.4	Opacity	Opaque
Kaolin	4.5	Color / oxidation	White (32)
Soda feldspar	2.0	/ reduction	Gray (8)
Zinc oxide	.8		
	100.0		

G 406 Semimat

Soda feldspar	57.88	Temperature	C/10
Barium carbonate	24.74	Surface @ C/10	Semimat
Whiting	12.61	Fluidity	Some
Bentonite	4.77	Stain penetration	Yes
		Opacity	Translucent
	100.00	Color / oxidation	Slight white (32)
		/ reduction	Gray (8)

G 407 White Semimat

Potash feldspar	41.0	Temperature	C/10-11
Kaolin	24.0	Surface @ C/10	Semimat
Whiting	18.0	Fluidity	Little
Flint	14.5	Stain penetration	Yes
Zinc oxide	2.5	Opacity	Translucent
		Color / oxidation	White (7)
	100.0	/ reduction	Off-white (8)

G 408 Opaque Semimat

Soda feldspar	78	Temperature	C/10-11
Whiting	10	Surface @ C/10	Semimat
Kaolin	10	Fluidity	Little
Bone ash	2	Stain penetration	Darks show
Zinc oxide	2	Opacity	Opaque
	___	Color / oxidation	White (7)
	102	/ reduction	Gray (8)

G 409 Barium Mat (Otis, Los Angeles, California)

Kingman feldspar	52.6	Temperature	C/10-11
Barium carbonate	21.0	Surface @ C/10	Semimat
Flint	10.5	Fluidity	Little
China clay	10.5	Stain penetration	Darks show
Dolomite	5.4	Opacity	Opaque
	___	Color / oxidation	Off-white (8)
	100.0	/ reduction	Gray (104)

G 410 Semimat

Kona feldspar	50.2	Temperature	C/10
Barium carbonate	19.8	Surface @ C/10	Semimat
Flint	9.9	Fluidity	Some
Kaolin	9.7	Stain penetration	Darks show
Spodumene	5.4	Opacity	Opaque
Dolomite	5.0	Color / oxidation	White (31)
	___	/ reduction	Gray (104)
	100.0		

G 411 Ackermann's Mat

Potash feldspar	47.01	Temperature	C/10
Silica	15.00	Surface @ C/10	Semimat
Talc	13.63	Fluidity	Fluid
Colemanite	11.68	Stain penetration	Darks show
Dolomite	8.11	Opacity	Opaque
E.P. kaolin	4.57	Color / oxidation	White (32)
		/ reduction	White (7)
	100.00		

G 412 Opaque Semimat

Potash feldspar	37.8	Temperature	C/10
Whiting	20.9	Surface @ C/10	Semimat
Kaolin	19.8	Fluidity	Some
Flint	15.8	Stain penetration	Darks show
Titanium dioxide	4.2	Opacity	Opaque
Zinc oxide	1.5	Color / oxidation	Off-white (30)
		/ reduction	Broken white-tan
	100.0		(6-31)

G 413 #S6 (Los Angeles State College, Los Angeles, California)

Silica	35	Temperature	C/10-11
Kingman feldspar	25	Surface @ C/10	Semimat
Dolomite	15	Fluidity	None
Whiting	10	Stain penetration	Darks show
Bentonite	10	Opacity	Opaque
Kaolin	5	Color / oxidation	Cream (15)
		/ reduction	White (7)
	100		

G 414 Opaque White

Potash feldspar	31.8	Temperature	C/10
Silica	28.1	Surface @ C/10	Semimat
Talc	15.2	Fluidity	Fluid
Colemanite	9.7	Stain penetration	Darks show
Dolomite	7.8	Opacity	Opaque
China clay	7.4	Color / oxidation	White (32)
	———	/ reduction	White (7)
	100.0		

G 415 Opaque Mat K-2

Potash feldspar	61.50	Temperature	C/10
Dolomite	10.10	Surface @ C/10	Mat
Opax	9.09	Fluidity	Some
Whiting	8.24	Stain penetration	None
Kaolin	5.66	Opacity	Opaque
Barium carbonate	5.41	Color / oxidation	White (7)
	———	/ reduction	Slight pink (48)
	100.00		

G 416 White Mat

Potash feldspar	60.2	Temperature	C/10-11
Kaolin	30.1	Surface @ C/10	Mat
Talc	4.8	Fluidity	Little
Bone ash	2.5	Stain penetration	Darks show
Whiting	2.4	Opacity	Opaque
	———	Color / oxidation	White (7)
	100.0	/ reduction	Gray (8)

G 417 Opaque

Potash feldspar	60	Temperature	C/10-11
Whiting	19	Surface @ C/10	Mat
China clay	16	Fluidity	Some
Zinc oxide	5	Stain penetration	None
	———	Opacity	Opaque
	100	Color / oxidation	White (32)
		/ reduction	White (7)

G 418 Mat #A

Kingman feldspar	54.27	Temperature	C/10
Barium carbonate	18.29	Surface @ C/10	Mat
Kentucky ball #4	8.24	Fluidity	Some
Whiting	6.43	Stain penetration	Darks show
Zinc oxide	6.43	Opacity	Opaque
Colemanite	4.53	Color / oxidation	White (32)
Rutile	1.81	/ reduction	Gray (8)
	———		
	100.00		

G 419 Malloy White

Potash feldspar	54.07	Temperature	C/10-11
Kentucky ball #4	24.90	Surface @ C/10	Mat
Dolomite	17.80	Fluidity	Little
Whiting	3.23	Stain penetration	Very darks show
	———	Opacity	Opaque
	100.00	Color / oxidation	White (32)
		/ reduction	Off-white (7)

G 420 Otis Bright Mat

Kingman feldspar	51.25	Temperature	C/10-11
Barium carbonate	17.91	Surface @ C/10	Mat
Zinc oxide	15.42	Fluidity	Little
China clay	10.41	Stain penetration	Darks show
Whiting	6.01	Opacity	Opaque
	_____	Color / oxidation	White (32)
	101.00	/ reduction	Off-white (8)

G 421 Opaque Mat

Potash feldspar	50.1	Temperature	C/10-12
Kentucky ball #4	19.0	Surface @ C/10	Mat
Whiting	18.0	Fluidity	Some
Spodumene	4.9	Stain penetration	Darks show
China clay	4.5	Opacity	Opaque
Zinc oxide	3.5	Color / oxidation	White (7)
	_____	/ reduction	Off-white (8)
	100.0		

G 422 Mat #G-3

Potash feldspar	51.03	Temperature	C/10-11
Barium carbonate	20.63	Surface @ C/10	Mat
Kentucky ball #4	9.81	Fluidity	Little
Whiting	8.70	Stain penetration	Darks show
Zinc oxide	7.88	Opacity	Opaque
Rutile	1.95	Color / oxidation	Broken white-cream (32-30)
	_____		
	100.00	/ reduction	Broken white-gray (7-104)

G 423 Fluid Mat

Kona feldspar	48.6	Temperature	C/10
Kaolin	25.0	Surface @ C/10	Mat
Dolomite	22.3	Fluidity	Fluid
Whiting	3.4	Stain penetration	Darks show
Zinc oxide	.7	Opacity	Opaque
	——	Color / oxidation	White (32)
	100.0	/ reduction	White (8)

G 424 Tan Mat

Potash feldspar	45	Temperature	C/10-11
Barium carbonate	18	Surface @ C/10	Mat
Rutile	13	Fluidity	Some
Kentucky ball #4	9	Stain penetration	Darks show
Whiting	8	Opacity	Opaque
Zinc oxide	7	Color / oxidation	Tan (28)
	——	/ reduction	Tan (24)
	100		

G 425 Cream Mat (San Diego State University, San Diego, California)

Potash feldspar	39.6	Temperature	C/10-11
Flint	18.5	Surface @ C/10	Mat
Talc	13.5	Fluidity	Some
Colemanite	11.1	Stain penetration	Darks show
Kentucky ball #4	8.3	Opacity	Opaque
Dolomite	7.8	Color / oxidation	Cream (29)
Red iron oxide	1.2	/ reduction	Gray (8)
	——		
	100.0		

G 426 Opaque White D 22 (Los Angeles State College, Los Angeles, California)

Nepheline syenite	36	Temperature	C/10-11
Kingsley kaolin	22	Surface @ C/10	Mat
Dolomite	14	Fluidity	None
Silica	14	Stain penetration	None
Whiting	8	Opacity	Opaque
Zinc oxide	6	Color / oxidation	White (32)
	⎯⎯	/ reduction	Off-white (8)
	100		

G 427 Fluid Mat #G

Kingman feldspar	35.11	Temperature	C/10
Nepheline syenite	25.70	Surface @ C/10	Mat
Barium carbonate	12.22	Fluidity	Fluid
Whiting	9.40	Stain penetration	Darks show
E.P. kaolin	8.17	Opacity	Opaque
Dolomite	5.64	Color / oxidation	White (32)
Silica	3.76	/ reduction	Gray (8)
	⎯⎯⎯		
	100.00		

G 428 Mat #MK 1

Kingman feldspar	34.71	Temperature	C/10-11
Flint	27.13	Surface @ C/10	Mat
Talc	11.20	Fluidity	Some
E.P. kaolin	10.93	Stain penetration	Darks show
Colemanite	9.63	Opacity	Opaque
Dolomite	6.40	Color / oxidation	White (6)
	⎯⎯⎯	/ reduction	White (7)
	100.00		

G 429 Jack's White Mat

Kaolin	33	Temperature	C/10-11
Dolomite	30	Surface @ C/10	Mat
Potash feldspar	25	Fluidity	Some
Flint	7	Stain penetration	Darks show
Whiting	5	Opacity	Opaque
	____	Color / oxidation	White (32)
	100	/ reduction	Broken white (7)

G 430 Otis Mat

Nepheline syenite	31.6	Temperature	C/10-11
China clay	21.2	Surface @ C/10	Mat
Flint	16.4	Fluidity	Some
Dolomite	12.6	Stain penetration	Darks show
Zinc oxide	11.3	Opacity	Opaque
Whiting	6.9	Color / oxidation	White (31)
	____	/ reduction	White (7)
	100.0		

G 431 Mat #OG 36

Delmonte feldspar	25.61	Temperature	C/10-11
Silica	24.51	Surface @ C/10	Mat
Talc	19.29	Fluidity	Little
Colemanite	13.33	Stain penetration	Darks show
Dolomite	8.77	Opacity	Opaque
Kentucky ball #4	8.49	Color / oxidation	White (32)
	____	/ reduction	White (27)
	100.00		

G 432 Mat D-4 (Los Angeles State College, Los Angeles, California)

Cornish stone	20	Temperature	C/10-11
Silica	20	Surface @ C/10	Mat
Kingman feldspar	15	Fluidity	Some
Talc	15	Stain penetration	Darks show
Colemanite	10	Opacity	Opaque
Dolomite	10	Color / oxidation	White (6)
Kaolin	10	/ reduction	White (32)
	100		

G 433 Opaque Tan

Kingman feldspar	54.84	Temperature	C/10-11
Dolomite	9.01	Surface @ C/10	Broken gloss and
Kentucky ball #4	8.69		semimat
Whiting	7.34	Fluidity	Some
Opax	5.43	Stain penetration	Darks show
E.P. kaolin	5.04	Opacity	Opaque
Rutile	4.83	Color / oxidation	Tan (30)
Barium carbonate	4.82	/ reduction	Broken tan (30-28)
	100.00		

G 434 Spotty Rutile Tan

Kingman feldspar	47.06	Temperature	C/10
Barium carbonate	19.79	Surface @ C/10	Mat
Kentucky ball #4	9.39	Fluidity	Fluid
Whiting	8.34	Stain penetration	Darks show
Rutile	7.84	Opacity	Opaque
Zinc oxide	7.58	Color / oxidation	Tan (29)
		/ reduction	Gray tan (grayed
	100.00		28)

Note: Broken and spotty color over dark clays

G 435 Semigloss Tan

Kingman feldspar	46.39	Temperature	C/10
Whiting	22.78	Surface @ C/10	Semigloss
E.P. kaolin	11.39	Fluidity	Some
Flint	11.39	Stain penetration	Darks show
Rutile	8.24	Opacity	Opaque
	———	Color / oxidation	Tan (21)
	100.19	/ reduction	Gray (146)

G 436 Mat Tan

Potash feldspar	40	Temperature	C/10-12
Hardwood ash	34	Surface @ C/10	Mat
Kentucky ball #4	24	Fluidity	Some
Bentonite	2	Stain penetration	Darks show
	———	Opacity	Opaque
	100	Color / oxidation	Tan (28)
		/ reduction	Tan (159)

G 437 Autumn Leaf

Lincoln clay	31.68	Temperature	C/10-11
Potash feldspar	25.01	Surface @ C/10	Semigloss
Dolomite	18.44	Fluidity	Little
Volcanic ash	10.34	Stain penetration	Darks show
Lepidolite	5.01	Opacity	Opaque
Flint	4.70	Color / oxidation	Broken tan (28)
Bone ash	3.08	/ reduction	Grayed tan (8-36)
Tin oxide	1.00		
Wollastonite	.74		
	———		
	100.00		

G 438 Reduction Yellow-brown

Kingman feldspar	30	Temperature	C/10
Whiting	24	Surface @ C/10	Mat
Flint	13	Fluidity	Fluid
E.P. kaolin	13	Stain penetration	None
Rutile	9	Opacity	Opaque
Colemanite	6	Color / oxidation	Tan (17)
Red iron oxide	5	/ reduction	Yellow-brown (159)
	100		

G 439 Opaque Tan

Flint	29.63	Temperature	C/10-11
Kingman feldspar	24.78	Surface @ C/10	Semigloss
Kaolin	17.97	Fluidity	Some
Whiting	17.64	Stain penetration	None
Rutile	5.98	Opacity	Opaque
Tin oxide	2.00	Color / oxidation	Tan (21)
Red iron oxide	2.00	/ reduction	Brown (156)
	100.00		

G 440 Waxy Yellow

Potash feldspar	60.00	Temperature	C/10-11
Whiting	18.41	Surface @ C/10	Mat
Kaolin	15.95	Fluidity	Some
Rutile	3.77	Stain penetration	Darks show
Red iron oxide	1.87	Opacity	Opaque
		Color / oxidation	Cream (40)
	100.00	/ reduction	Grayed yellow (grayed 12)

G 441 Yellow

Potash feldspar	40.66	Temperature	C/10
Barium carbonate	16.47	Surface @ C/10	Mat
Whiting	14.66	Fluidity	Fluid
Kentucky ball #4	7.80	Stain penetration	Darks show
Magnesium carbonate	7.80	Opacity	Translucent
Zinc oxide	6.09	Color / oxidation	Yellow (24)
Yellow ochre	4.81	/ reduction	Grayed yellow (18)
Rutile	1.71		
	100.00		

G 442 Mustard

Potash feldspar	34.4	Temperature	C/10
Nepheline syenite	25.2	Surface @ C/10	Mat
Barium carbonate	12.7	Fluidity	Fluid
Whiting	9.2	Stain penetration	None
Kaolin	7.8	Opacity	Opaque
Flint	3.7	Color / oxidation	Yellow-tan (22)
Red iron oxide	3.7	/ reduction	Broken gray-brown
Dolomite	3.2		(138)
	99.9		

G 443 Rutile #K

Potash feldspar	60.1	Temperature	C/10
Calcium carbonate	13.6	Surface @ C/10	Mat
Kentucky ball #4	8.7	Fluidity	Fluid
Barium carbonate	5.6	Stain penetration	None
E.P. kaolin	5.6	Opacity	Opaque
Rutile	4.3	Color / oxidation	Orange (46)
Magnesium	2.1	/ reduction	Broken white and gray
	100.0		(7-104)

G 444 Mustard 10

Potash feldspar	48.95	Temperature	C/10
Whiting	17.83	Surface @ C/10	Mat
E.P. kaolin	14.61	Fluidity	Fluid
Rutile	8.88	Stain penetration	Darks show
Zinc oxide	5.31	Opacity	Opaque
Red iron oxide	4.42	Color / oxidation	Broken yellow (12)
	————	/ reduction	Broken orange (58)
	100.00		

G 445 Oxidation White and Orange

Kingman feldspar	45	Temperature	C/10
Whiting	22	Surface @ C/10	Semigloss
Silica	13	Fluidity	Very fluid
E.P. kaolin	11	Stain penetration	Darks show
Rutile	6	Opacity	Opaque
Lithium carbonate	5	Color / oxidation	Broken white and orange (15 & 72)
	————	/ reduction	Broken white-tan (8-28)
	102		

G 446 John Mason's Red

Potash feldspar	72.5	Temperature	C/10
Colemanite	10.9	Surface @ C/10	Gloss
Whiting	7.2	Fluidity	Fluid
Flint	7.2	Stain penetration	Yes
Tin oxide	1.1	Opacity	Transparent
Copper carbonate	1.1	Color / oxidation	Green (121)
	————	/ reduction	Grayed red (50)
	100.0		

G447 Reduction Red

Kingman feldspar	51.80	Temperature	C/10
Flint	25.55	Surface @ C/10	Gloss
Whiting	8.75	Fluidity	Fluid
Colemanite	6.50	Stain penetration	Yes
Dolomite	2.30	Opacity	Transparent
Zinc oxide	2.20	Color / oxidation	Green (143)
Tin oxide	1.00	/ reduction	Red (52)
Copper carbonate	1.00		
Red iron oxide	.90		

100.00

G448 Reduction Dark Red

Potash feldspar	42.5	Temperature	C/10
Flint	25.0	Surface @ C/10	Gloss
Colemanite	17.5	Fluidity	Fluid
Barium carbonate	10.0	Stain penetration	Yes
Whiting	2.5	Opacity	Transparent
Copper carbonate	1.0	Color / oxidation	Green (121)
Tin oxide	1.0	/ reduction	Dark red (49)
Iron oxide, red	.5		

100.0

G 449 Reduction Broken Reds

Potash feldspar	35.24	Temperature	C/10-11
Flint	35.24	Surface @ C/10	Semimat
Whiting	15.40	Fluidity	Some
Colemanite	10.57	Stain penetration	Darks show
Tin oxide	1.68	Opacity	Translucent
China clay	1.45	Color / oxidation	Baby blue (86)
Copper carbonate	.42	/ reduction	Broken white, red, and purple

100.00

G 450 Red ML 2A

Potash feldspar	31.14	Temperature	C/10
Flint	29.36	Surface @ C/10	Gloss
Colemanite	14.10	Fluidity	Fluid
Zinc oxide	8.27	Stain penetration	Yes
Barium carbonate	6.70	Opacity / oxidation	Transparent
Talc	6.43	Color / oxidation	Pale blue (87)
Copper carbonate	2.00	Opacity / reduction	Opaque
Tin oxide	1.50	Color / reduction	Blood red (dark 54)
	99.50		

G 451 Mat Blue

Nepheline syenite	48.1	Temperature	C/10-12
Barium carbonate	37.3	Surface @ C/10	Mat
Flint	7.5	Fluidity	Little
Kentucky ball #4	7.1	Stain penetration	None
Copper carbonate	4.0	Opacity	Opaque
		Color / oxidation	Broken blues (91-81)
	104.0	/ reduction	Broken blues (92-90)

G 452 Opaque Blue

Potash feldspar	47.4	Temperature	C/10-12
Kaolin	24.7	Surface @ C/10	Dry mat
Dolomite	22.2	Fluidity	None
Whiting	3.4	Stain penetration	None
Soda ash	1.5	Opacity	Opaque
Black cobalt oxide	.6	Color / oxidation	Blue (98)
Green chromium oxide	.2	/ reduction	Blue (98)
	100.0		

G 453 Reduction Blue-green G2

Potash feldspar	45	Temperature	C/10
Whiting	22	Surface @ C/10	Gloss
E.P. kaolin	20	Fluidity	Some
Silica	11	Stain penetration	Yes
Red iron oxide	2	Opacity	Transparent
	——	Color / oxidation	Tan (18)
	100	/ reduction	Blue-green (139)

G 454 Oxidation Blue

Potash feldspar	44.25	Temperature	C/10
Barium carbonate	18.53	Surface @ C/10	Mat
Kentucky ball #4	8.81	Fluidity	Some
Whiting	7.81	Stain penetration	Darks show
Rutile	7.63	Opacity	Translucent
Zinc oxide	7.08	Color / oxidation	Blue
Bone ash	4.70	/ reduction	Broken gray (103)
Copper carbonate	.70		
Cobalt oxide	.49		
	100.00		

G 455 Reduction Blue-gray

Potash feldspar	42.7	Temperature	C/10
Barium carbonate	17.3	Surface @ C/10	Dry mat
Whiting	15.4	Fluidity	Fluid
Plastic vetrox clay	8.2	Stain penetration	Darks show
Vanadium pentoxide	8.2	Opacity	Opaque
Zinc oxide	6.4	Color / oxidation	Off-white (30)
Rutile	1.8	/ reduction	Blue-gray (96)
	100.0		

G 456 Celedon

Nepheline syenite	42.57	Temperature	C/10-11
Silica	27.50	Surface @ C/10	Gloss
Whiting	17.90	Fluidity	Some
Kaolin	10.11	Stain penetration	Yes
Red iron oxide	1.92	Opacity	Transparent
	———	Color / oxidation	Yellow (13)
	100.00	/ reduction	Blue-green (light 130)

G 457 Celedon

Kingman feldspar	30.20	Temperature	C/10-12
Kaolin	27.70	Surface @ C/10	Semimat
Whiting	22.28	Fluidity	None
Flint	18.36	Stain penetration	Darks show
Red iron oxide	1.46	Opacity	Translucent
	———	Color / oxidation	Tan (24)
	100.00	/ reduction	Grayed tan (grayed 150)

G 458 Celedon

Whiting	29.75	Temperature	C/10-11
Potash feldspar	29.37	Surface @ C/10	Semimat
China clay	21.04	Fluidity	Some
Silica	17.55	Stain penetration	Yes
Red iron oxide	2.29	Opacity	Translucent
	———	Color / oxidation	Yellow-brown (157)
	100.00	/ reduction	Green (141)
		Note: Apply thick	

G 459 Celedon

China clay	27.53	Temperature	C/10-11
Potash feldspar	27.24	Surface @ C/10	Mat
Whiting	24.03	Fluidity	Little
Flint	16.02	Stain penetration	Darks show
Red iron oxide	2.65	Opacity	Translucent
Zinc oxide	2.53	Color / oxidation	Buff (28)
		/ reduction	Gray-brown (146)
	100.00		

G 460 Khaki

Potash feldspar	56.5	Temperature	C/10-11
Flint	22.9	Surface @ C/10	Gloss
Red iron oxide	9.2	Fluidity	Some
Whiting	6.9	Stain penetration	None
Kaolin	4.5	Opacity	Opaque
		Color / oxidation	Olive-black
	100.0	/ reduction	Broken brown-black

G 461 Khaki

Kentucky ball #4	24.7	Temperature	C/10
Flint	24.6	Surface @ C/10	Gloss
Potash feldspar	19.9	Fluidity	Some
Whiting	14.9	Stain penetration	None
Red iron oxide	14.7	Opacity	Opaque
Tin oxide	1.2	Color / oxidation	Olive-black (dark 155)
	100.0	/ reduction	Metallic brown-black

G 462 Khaki

Potash feldspar	50.0	Temperature	C/10-12
China clay	19.2	Surface @ C/10	Mat
Silica	13.5	Fluidity	None
Red iron oxide	11.3	Stain penetration	None
Whiting	6.5	Opacity	Opaque
	———	Color / oxidation	Dark brown (73)
	100.5	/ reduction	Metallic dark brown

G 463 Fall Brown

Potash feldspar	49.1	Temperature	C/10-11
Barium carbonate	19.9	Surface @ C/10	Mat
Kentucky ball #4	9.4	Fluidity	Little
Whiting	8.2	Stain penetration	Darks show
Zinc oxide	7.6	Opacity	Opaque
Red iron oxide	3.9	Color / oxidation	Brown (35)
Rutile	1.9	/ reduction	Broken browns (35-158)
	———		
	100.0		

G 464 Reduction Iron Brown

Kingman feldspar	39.15	Temperature	C/10
Flint	25.27	Surface @ C/10	Gloss
Whiting	16.56	Fluidity	Some
Red iron oxide	9.29	Stain penetration	None
E.P. kaolin	8.83	Opacity	Opaque
Bentonite	.90	Color / oxidation	Dark yellow-brown (dark 158)
	———		
	100.00	/ reduction	Mirror yellow-brown (dark 158)

G 465 Parmala #11

Potash feldspar	32.95	Temperature	C/10
Kaolin	22.73	Surface @ C/10	Gloss and semigloss
Flint	15.87	Fluidity	Some
Manganese carbonate	13.26	Stain penetration	Some
Whiting	11.38	Opacity	Opaque
Zinc oxide	2.38	Color / oxidation	Brown (156)
Barium carbonate	1.43	/ reduction	Brown (154)
	100.00		

G 466 Temmoku

Flint	25.0	Temperature	C/10
Potash feldspar	23.0	Surface @ C/10	Gloss
Whiting	18.0	Fluidity	Some
Lincoln clay	12.5	Stain penetration	None
Kentucky ball #4	12.5	Opacity	Opaque
Red iron oxide	9.0	Color / oxidation	Dark yellow-brown (dark 157)
	100.0	/ reduction	Mirror broken brown-black

G 467 Reduction Brown-black

Potash feldspar	68.3	Temperature	C/10
Silica	8.6	Surface @ C/10	Semigloss
Dolomite	8.6	Fluidity	Some
Red iron oxide	8.6	Stain penetration	None
Kentucky ball #4	4.3	Opacity	Opaque
Bone ash	1.6	Color / oxidation	Black (113)
	100.0	/ reduction	Broken brown-black

G 468 Temmoku Black

Potash feldspar	50.46	Temperature	C/10
Flint	18.37	Surface @ C/10	Gloss
Whiting	14.41	Fluidity	Some
Red iron oxide	9.68	Stain penetration	None
Kaolin	6.51	Opacity	Opaque
Cobalt carbonate	.57	Color / oxidation	Mirror black (113)
		/ reduction	Mirror black (113),
	100.00		brown where thin

G 469 Aventurine

Colemanite	38.46	Temperature	C/10
Red iron oxide	23.08	Surface @ C/10	Gloss
Potash feldspar	23.08	Fluidity	Fluid
Flint	15.38	Stain penetration	None
		Opacity	Opaque
	100.00	Color / oxidation	Broken black, brown, ochre, and some gold fleck where thick
		/ reduction	Metallic brown-black

G 470 Oxidation Charcoal

Potash feldspar	34.2	Temperature	C/10
Flint	25.0	Surface @ C/10	Semigloss
Magnesium carbonate	14.1	Fluidity	Some
Whiting	12.2	Stain penetration	None
Kentucky ball #4	8.2	Opacity	Opaque
Zinc oxide	2.4	Color / oxidation	Charcoal (145)
Chromium oxide	2.4	/ reduction	Dark brown (154)
Barium carbonate	1.5		
	100.0		

G 471 Metallic Brown-black

Flint	25	Temperature	C/10
Kingman feldspar	20	Surface @ C/10	Gloss
Whiting	20	Fluidity	Fluid
E.P. kaolin	20	Stain penetration	None
Red iron oxide	15	Opacity	Opaque
	___	Color / oxidation	Brown-black
	100	/ reduction	Metallic brown-black

G 472 Reduction Metallic Charcoal

Soda feldspar	23.08	Temperature	C/10
Boric acid	23.08	Surface @ C/10	Semigloss
Red iron oxide	23.08	Fluidity	Fluid
Flint	15.38	Stain penetration	None
Whiting	15.38	Opacity	Opaque
	_____	Color / oxidation	Broken black, brown,
	100.00		ochres
		/ reduction	Metallic charcoal
			(115)

Porcelain Glaze Formulas   *Cone/11 and Up*

Early man used primitive methods of decorating clays with powdered minerals. Some were colored clays and others were low-temperature fluxing materials mixed with colorants to produce the first glazes. In time, the introduction of refined flint, clays, opacifying agents, different types of fluxes, and an increased number of metallic oxides enlarged the scope of glazes. As the ceramists kept pace with the increased knowledge of the glaze craft, higher temperatures were used, which gave a glaze more durability and less porosity. Ultimately, white translucent porcelain was created. Some of the most beautiful porcelains are those of soft white and subtle texture glazes produced in China. Many of those pieces produced during the Ming, T'ang, and Ch'inen Lung dynasties (from A.D. 600 to early 1900) had little or no decoration, except for ornaments in relief or an engraved design, which are perceptible when the object is held to the light. Two of the most famous Chinese decorations process are flambé porcelain and famille verte.

Flambé porcelain is the process of "flashing" whereby metallic oxides in the glaze were affected by lack of oxygen in the kiln. Under ordinary oxidation firing, the oxygen in the air would combine with the metal to fuse into an oxide. The introduction of thick smoke absorbed the oxygen and caused the oxygen to leave the oxide, thus giving the glaze a different color, resulting from pure metal deposited on the surface of the glaze or held in suspension within the glaze. The Chinese were able, entirely by this process, to imitate a fruit with its many varied and wondrous tints.

Famille verte is the enameling of porcelain. Several colors were applied as an understain, and porcelain glaze applied over these and fired. The piece was finished with overglaze "enamel" and fired in a sufficiently low temperature to fuse the enamel to the porcelain. These later decorations stand out in a slight relief. These examples just barely serve to introduce the possible porcelain glaze techniques.

Glazes that mature when fired at a temperature range of 2336° to 2700°F. are known as porcelain glazes, but some porcelain-type glazes are fired at lower temperatures. Porcelain glaze receives its name from the use and association with porcelain clays. Most probably, the clay and glaze had their origin in China at the same time and region. The most common materials used in the glazes are clay, silica, and flux (usually feldspar), barium carbonate, magnesium carbonate, whiting, and colemanite. This glaze is hard, not easily scratched, resistant to most acids and alkalines, mechanically strong, and waterproof. In general, the glaze formulas have few components and thus are simple to prepare and apply.

The formulas that follow are organized into two temperature groups of Cone/11 to 12 and Cone/13 and up: subdivided as to gloss, semigloss, and mat surfaces; then distinguished as to transparent, translucent, and opaque qualities; and followed by color and special effects.

CONE/11 TO CONE/12

G 473 Gloss

Flint	44.2	Temperature	C/11-12
Calcined kaolin	28.0	Surface @ C/11	Gloss
Potash feldspar	16.2	Fluidity	Little
Calcium carbonate	11.6	Stain penetration	Yes
	_____	Opacity	Clear, thin
	100.0		Translucent, thick
		Color / oxidation	White (6)
		/ reduction	White (7)

G 474 Fluid Gloss

Potash feldspar	34.5	Temperature	C/11
Zinc oxide	22.8	Surface @ C/11	Gloss
Whiting	15.9	Fluidity	Fluid
Flint	15.9	Stain penetration	Yes
Kona feldspar	10.9	Opacity	Clear, thin
			Translucent, thick
	100.0	Color / oxidation	White (32)
		/ reduction	White (7)

G 475 Warm Tan

Buckingham feldspar	23.4	Temperature	C/11
Potash feldspar	21.0	Surface @ C/11	Semigloss
Whiting	21.0	Fluidity	Some
Flint	12.6	Stain penetration	Yes
Kaolin	11.6	Opacity	Translucent
Tin oxide	7.0	Color / oxidation	Buff (40)
Yellow ochre	2.0	/ reduction	Brown (156)
Rutile	1.4		
	100.0		

G 476 Celadon

Flint	36.3	Temperature	C/11
Potash feldspar	26.9	Surface @ C/11	Semigloss
Whiting	26.9	Fluidity	Some
China clay	5.4	Stain penetration	Darks show
Buckingham feldspar	3.0	Opacity	Translucent
Red iron oxide	1.0	Color / oxidation	Buff (28)
Yellow ochre	.5	/ reduction	Light green-gray (134)
	100.0		

G 477 Celadon

Flint	35.5	Temperature	C/11
Whiting	21.2	Surface @ C/11	Gloss
Potash feldspar	19.9	Fluidity	Some
Kaolin	9.2	Stain penetration	Yes
Buckingham feldspar	8.0	Opacity	Transparent
Yellow ochre	5.9	Color / oxidation	Slight yellow (24)
Red iron oxide	.3	/ reduction	Slight gray-green (134)
	100.0		

G 478 Grayed Blue Celadon

Flint	32.7	Temperature	C/11-12
Kaolin	19.3	Surface @ C/11	Gloss
Whiting	19.3	Fluidity	Little
Potash feldspar	16.7	Stain penetration	Darks show
Kona feldspar	10.5	Opacity	Translucent
Red iron oxide	1.3	Color / oxidation	Grayed blue
Cobalt oxide	.2		(grayed 98)
	———	/ reduction	Grayed blue
	100.0		(grayed 91)

G 479 Green Celadon

Potash feldspar	30.0	Temperature	C/11
Flint	30.0	Surface @ C/11	Gloss
Whiting	18.0	Fluidity	Fluid
Buckingham feldspar	10.8	Stain penetration	Yes
Kaolin	8.0	Opacity	Transparent
Black iron oxide	2.8	Color / oxidation	Slight yellow-brown
Iron chromate	.4		(147)
	———	/ reduction	Green (129)
	100.0		

G 480 Reduction Rust-brown

Monmouth clay	40.0	Temperature	C/11
Potash feldspar	19.0	Surface @ C/11	Gloss
Albany slip	19.0	Fluidity	Some
Buckingham feldspar	7.0	Stain penetration	None
Kaolin	6.7	Opacity	Opaque
Whiting	6.7	Color / oxidation	Dark brown (153)
Burnt umber	1.6	/ reduction	Rust-brown (dark 74)
	———		
	100.0		

G 481 Reduction Metallic Purple

Volcanic ash	37	Temperature	C/11
Potash feldspar	30	Surface @ C/11	Semigloss
Local red clay	20	Fluidity	Some
Hardwood ash	8	Stain penetration	None
Red iron oxide	5	Opacity	Opaque
	———	Color / oxidation	Dark brown (73)
	100	/ reduction	Metallic purple (dark 107)

G 482 Semimat Reduction Black

Flint	30.5	Temperature	C/11-12
Whiting	26.0	Surface @ C/11	Semimat
Kaolin	13.0	Fluidity	Little
Cobalt oxide	8.5	Stain penetration	None
Iron chromate	8.0	Opacity	Opaque
Potash feldspar	7.0	Color / oxidation	Blue-black (90-113)
E.P. kaolin	7.0	/ reduction	Broken black (113)
	———		
	100.0		

CONE/13 AND UP

G 483 Translucent Gloss

Potash feldspar	42	Temperature	C/13
Flint	27	Surface @ C/13	Gloss
Whiting	18	Fluidity	Some
Kentucky ball #4	10	Stain penetration	Yes
E.P. kaolin	3	Opacity	Clear, thin
			Translucent, thick
	100	Color / oxidation	Some white
		/ reduction	Some white

G 484 Opaque Gloss

Potash feldspar	70	Temperature	C/13
Flint	25	Surface @ C/13	Gloss
Kaolin	4	Fluidity	Little
Dolomite	1	Stain penetration	Yes
		Opacity	Translucent, thin
	100		Opaque, thick
		Color / oxidation	White (7)
		/ reduction	White (8)
		Note: Cracks	

G 485 Gloss

Flint	50	Temperature	C/13-14
Calcined kaolin	26	Surface @ C/13	Gloss
Potash feldspar	14	Fluidity	Little
Dolomite	9	Stain penetration	Yes
		Opacity	Translucent, thin
	99		Opaque, thick
		Color / oxidation	White (32)
		/ reduction	White (7)

G 486 Gloss

Flint	47	Temperature	C/15
Potash feldspar	13	Surface @ C/15	Gloss
Aluminum oxide	13	Fluidity	Some
Whiting	10	Stain penetration	Darks show
Buckingham feldspar	10	Opacity	Translucent, thin
E.P. kaolin	7		Opaque, thick
	———	Color / oxidation	White (32)
	100	/ reduction	White (7)

G 487 Semigloss

Flint	48	Temperature	C/15
Aluminum oxide	26	Surface @ C/15	Semigloss
Potash feldspar	10	Fluidity	Little
Kona feldspar	6	Stain penetration	Darks show
Whiting	6	Opacity	Translucent
Calcined kaolin	4	Color / oxidation	White (32)
	———	/ reduction	White (7)
	100		

Slip Glazes

Slip glazes are naturally occuring glaze-making clays that are a result of glacial clay materials sorted by stream-water action and deposited in lakes created by the melting of the glacial ice. This clay is a mixture of all kinds of rock and clay materials over which the ice has traveled. Therefore, the clay deposits will be a varied mixture and often contain a large amount of feldspars and other materials. A number of beds are found in Europe, and in the United States in Indiana, Michigan, and, the most popular, Albany, New York (known as "Albany slip"). Oriental potters have used slip glazes extensively, and in the United States the commercial use of modified Albany slip is for electrical porcelain insulators and cooking ware.

Slip glazes have several desirable properties; they develop very little crazing, they have a long firing range, are inexpensive, and easy to mix and use. The natural color range is limited but includes yellowish brown, brownish black, dark brown, and tan. Even with such limitations, the Chinese were able to achieve interesting texture and subtle colors. These include hare's fur, temmoku, oil spot, mirror black, and partridge feather glazes.

By testing the slip glazes on the individual clays, various and interesting results can be achieved and dull and lifeless glazes can be avoided. Light-color clay forms will give some slip glazes a warm amber or rich brown color, while dark clay forms lend themselves to dark rust-brown and black colors. The following glaze formulas are but a suggestion of the possible slip glazes.

Slip Glaze Formulas

SG 1 Black

Albany slip	95.2	Temperature	C/8-9
Cobalt oxide	2.8	Surface @ C/8	Gloss
Black iron oxide	2.0	Surface @ C/9R	Semimat
	———	Fluidity	Some
	100.0	Stain penetration	None
		Opacity	Opaque
		Color / oxidation	Mirror black (113)
		/ reduction	Metallic black (113)

SG 2 Oil Spot

Albany slip	84.74	Temperature	C/9-10
Yellow ochre	8.47	Surface @ C/9	Gloss
Lepidolite	4.28	Surface @ C/10R	Semigloss
Bone ash	1.69	Fluidity	Little
Colemanite	.82	Stain penetration	None
	———	Opacity	Opaque
	100.00	Color / oxidation	Oil spots, black (113)
		/ reduction	Dark brown (154)

SG 3 Oxidation Oil Spot

Albany slip	80	Temperature	C/9-10
Red iron oxide	8	Surface @ C/9	Gloss
Rutile	8	Surface @ C/10R	Mat
Potash feldspar	4	Fluidity	Some
	____	Stain penetration	None
	100	Opacity	Opaque
		Color / oxidation	Oil spots, brown (dark 156)
		/ reduction	Metallic black (113)

SG 4 Oil Spot

Albany slip	77	Temperature	C/9-10
Spodumene	13	Surface @ C/9	Gloss
Yellow ochre	9	Fluidity	Some
Red iron oxide	1	Stain penetration	None
	____	Opacity	Opaque
	100	Color / oxidation	Oil spots, black (113)
		/ reduction	Dark brown (154)

SG 5 Brown

Albany slip	75	Temperature	C/8-10
Nepheline syenite	10	Surface @ C/8	Gloss
Red iron oxide	5	Surface @ C/10R	Mat
Borax	5	Fluidity	Little
Rutile	5	Stain penetration	None
	____	Opacity	Opaque
	100	Color / oxidation	Dark brown (154)
		/ reduction	Black (113)

SG 6 Oxidation Oil Spot

Albany slip	73	Temperature	C/8-10
Burnt sienna	9	Surface @ C/8	Gloss
Potash feldspar	9	Surface @ C/9R	Mat
Red iron oxide	5	Fluidity	Little
Hardwood ash	4	Stain penetration	None
	——	Opacity	Opaque
	100	Color / oxidation	Oil spots, mirror black (113)
		/ reduction	Metallic charcoal (145)

SG 7 Mat

Albany slip	70	Temperature	C/9-10
Zinc oxide	30	Surface @ C/9	Mat
	——	Fluidity	Little
	100	Stain penetration	Darks show
		Opacity	Translucent
		Color / oxidation	Yellow-green (138)
		/ reduction	Brown (156)

SG 8 Mat Brown

Albany slip	68	Temperature	C/9-10
Spodumene	17	Surface @ C/9	Mat
Whiting	6	Fluidity	Fluid
Rutile	5	Stain penetration	None
Red iron oxide	4	Opacity	Opaque
	——	Color / reduction	Rich brown (50)
	100		

SG 9 Oxidation Yellow-brown

Albany slip	62	Temperature	C/8-10
Nepheline syenite	34	Surface @ C/9	Gloss
Spodumene	3	Fluidity	Little
Tin oxide	1	Stain penetration	Dark show
	‾‾‾	Opacity	Translucent
	100	Color / oxidation	Yellow-brown
			(dark 35)
		/ reduction	Brown (156)

SG 10 Reduction Metallic

Barnard black	60	Temperature	C/9-10
Cornwall stone	25	Surface @ C/9	Semigloss
Whiting	10	Surface @ C/10R	Mat
Red iron oxide	5	Fluidity	None
	‾‾‾	Stain penetration	None
	100	Opacity	Opaque
		Color / oxidation	Black (113)
		/ reduction	Metallic charcoal
			(145)

SG 11 Albany Slip

Albany slip	50	Temperature	C/8-9
Whiting	20	Surface @ C/9R	Mat
Spodumene	16	Fluidity	Little
Red iron oxide	10	Stain penetration	Very darks show
Rutile	4	Opacity	Opaque
	———	Color / oxidation	Yellow-brown
	100		(broken 35)
		/ reduction	Red-brown (50)

SG 12 Oil Spot

Albany slip	46.1	Temperature	C/9-10
Potash feldspar	37.0	Surface @ C/9	Semigloss
Kentucky ball #4	9.2	Surface @ C/10R	Mat
Red iron oxide	4.5	Fluidity	Little
Borax	2.2	Stain penetration	None
Rutile	1.0	Opacity	Opaque
	———	Color / oxidation	Oil spot, brown-black
	100.0	/ reduction	Brown (50)

Raku Glazes

There are two common techniques of making raku in the United States. In the bisque fire technique, the object is made by hand or on the wheel; when dry, it is bisque-fired. The object is glazed and placed in a cold or slightly warm kiln and fired to the desired temperature. The hot object is removed from the kiln with tongs and placed in water to cool or in a metal container filled with fine wood chips or shredded paper and covered with a lid to create a reduction atmosphere. This dense, carbon-filled atmosphere has a low oxygen content, and thus causes the clay to turn dark and the metallic oxides in the glaze to turn colors different from what they would be in an oxidation firing. Sometimes the oxides will deposit a thin film on the glaze surface that has a bright metallic look; this is known as "luster." After three minutes, the object is removed from the container and dunked in water to cool. The clay will be black and, depending upon the type, the glaze color could range from white to copper luster. (When making rakuware for food purposes, avoid using glazes that have high lead content to avoid lead poisoning.)

In the wet fire technique, the object is made by hand or wheel-thrown, using a highly porous and coarse clay. While still wet, the object is covered with an engobe-type glaze. This wet object is placed in a 1700° F. kiln. The resulting steam creates a protective envelope around the object and prevents it from exploding. Upon reaching the desired temperature, the object is removed from the kiln and handled the same way as in the bisque fire technique.

The formulas listed were tested and the results analyzed the same way as for the other glaze formulas.

Raku Glaze Formulas

RG 1 Lead Gloss

White lead	82	Temperature	C/012
Flint	14	Surface @ C/012	Gloss
Colemanite	4	Fluidity	Some flow
	———	Stain penetration	Yes
	100	Opacity	Transparent .
		Color / reduction	Light yellow (3)
		/ oxidation	Light yellow (12)

RG 2 Selenium Raku (Ohio State University, Columbus, Ohio)

Ferro Frit 5301	72.72	Temperature	C/012
Borax	18.18	Surface @ C/012	Bright gloss
Bentonite	4.55	Fluidity	Some
Selenium	4.55	Stain penetration	Yes
	———	Opacity	Transparent
	100.00	Color / reduction	Clear
		/ oxidation	Clear
		Note: Crackle	

RG 3 Frit IV 48 Raku

Frit IV 48	76.2	Temperature	C/09
Ferro Frit 5301	14.3	Surface @ C/09	Gloss
China clay	4.7	Fluidity	Some
	———	Stain penetration	Yes
	95.2	Opacity	Transparent
		Color / reduction	Clear
		/ oxidation	Clear
		Opacity	Translucent
Selenium	4.8 {	Color / reduction	Pale turquoise (88)
		/ oxidation	Pale turquoise (86)

RG 4 Colemanite (Walter Chapman, Mesa College, San Diego, California)

Colemanite	69.8	Temperature	C/06
Plastic vitrox	30.2	Surface @ C/06	Gloss
	——	Fluidity	Little
	100.0	Stain penetration	Yes
		Opacity	Transparent
		Color / reduction	Clear
		/ oxidation	Clear

RG 5 Lead Clear

White lead	61	Temperature	C/012
Flint	28	Surface @ C/012	Gloss
Colemanite	8	Fluidity	Some
China clay	4	Stain penetration	Yes
	——	Opacity	Transparent
	101	Color / reduction	Slight yellow (5)
		/ oxidation	Slight yellow (5)
		Note: Some cracks	

RG 6 Frit Lead Gloss

White lead	58	Temperature	C/012
Flint	20	Surface @ C/012	Gloss
Ferro Frit 3124	14	Fluidity	Some
Soda ash	8	Stain penetration	Yes
	——	Opacity	Transparent
	100	Color / reduction	Clear
		/ oxidation	Clear

RG 7 Silver White

White lead	46	Temperature	C/012
Ferro Frit 5301	27	Surface @ C/012	Gloss
Flint	12	Fluidity	Some
Tin oxide	7	Stain penetration	Yes
Soda feldspar	5	Opacity	Opaque, thick
Zircopax	3		Translucent, thin
	——	Color / reduction	Silver-white (6)
	100	/ oxidation	Slight yellow-white (16)

RG 8 Semigloss

Red lead	41.27	Temperature	C/09
Flint	35.36	Surface @ C/09	Semigloss
Borax	10.72	Fluidity	Little
Boric acid	10.10	Stain penetration	Yes
China clay	2.55	Opacity	Transparent
	——	Color / reduction	Clear, slight yellow
	100.00	/ oxidation	Clear, slight yellow

RG 9 Frit 5301

Ferro Frit 5301	37.4	Temperature	C/012
White lead	27.1	Surface @ C/012	Bright gloss
Flint	10.3	Fluidity	Some
Boric acid	10.3	Stain penetration	Yes
Borax	8.4	Opacity	Transparent
	——	Color / reduction	Clear
	93.5	/ oxidation	Clear
Copper oxide	4.7	Stain penetration	No
Tin oxide	1.8	Opacity	Opaque
	——	Color / reduction	Rainbow, metallic
	100.0	/ oxidation	Dark turquoise (81)

RG 10 Green

Frit 5301	48	Temperature	C/016
White lead	26	Surface @ C/016	Gloss
Copper carbonate	19	Fluidity	Little
Flint	7	Stain penetration	None
	————	Opacity	Opaque
	100	Color / reduction	Browns, metallic
		/ oxidation	Green-black (dark 97)

Raku Glaze Colorants

Glaze color is a very significant property and is affected by many influences (see the Glaze Colorants section below). One of the most interesting aspects of raku glaze colors is the heavy reduction technique. Here the glazed clay form is taken from the hot kiln, placed in a metal container filled with wood chips, and the lid placed down tight. The hot clay burns the wood, creating a dense smoke that turns the clay black and causes colorants in the glaze to produce many unusual effects. Some glazes turn from pale green to red, copper green to luster, and some blues to greens. The most engrossing metamorphosis is the change of metallic oxides to pure metal that becomes deposited on the surface of the glaze. This deposit can be bright copper, silver gray, golden, reddish, or luster, depending upon the metallic oxide used in the glaze. The Raku Colorants Chart (p. 271) is a guide recommending colorants and percentages with the colors resulting from oxidation and heavy reduction atmosphere character. Many other colorants can be used and are listed in the Glaze Colorants section.

Raku Glaze Colorants Chart

Colorant	Percentage	Oxidation Color	Reduction Color
Chrome oxide	3.0	Chrome green (dark 122)	Chrome green with golden metallic areas (dark 122)
Cobalt oxide	1.5	Dark cobalt blue (89)	Dark cobalt blue with some reddish areas (89)
Copper carbonate	.5	Pale turquoise (86)	Pale turquoise (86)
Copper carbonate	2.0	Medium turquoise (83)	Medium green with copper metallic surface (125)
Iron oxide, red	1.0	Very pale cream (6)	Very pale cream (6)
Iron oxide, red	10.0	Medium grayed tan (28)	Medium grayed yellow with some luster areas
Manganese carbonate	4.0	Dark purple-brown (154)	Brown-black with copper metallic surface (154)
Nickel oxide	4.0	Light gray (104)	Light gray (104)
Potassium bichromate	3.0	Grayed yellow (148)	Grayed yellow with reddish metallic surface (148)
Rutile	5.0	Warm tan (21)	Cool tan (21)
Stain, pink	5.0	Pale pink (46)	Pale pink (46)
Uranium	6.0	Yellow (4)	Yellow with opalescent metallic areas (4)
Vanadium pentoxide	6.0	Opalescent white (good over white and colored englobes) (4)	Clear, slight yellow (4)

NOTE: Raku glaze No. RG 3 was used as a base for the above testing.

Glaze Colorants

Extensive research being conducted in industry and by individuals interested in colorants is making available new information about the chemistry of colors, their composition, and preparation. This is showing up in the new commercially made stains of the last ten years. As a point of reference, the early Chinese ceramists had a limited number of colorants, mainly copper and iron, and with these were able to achieve an extensive amount and variety of ceramic colors and textures.

Colored glazes may be produced multitudinously for many oxides, and a number of minerals for colorants are available. The oxides, opacifiers, and minerals include the following (the italicized items are the most commonly used):

Antimony
Burnt umber
Cadmiun (oxide and sulfide)
Cerium
Chromium oxide (black and *green*)
Cobalt (*carbonate*, chloride, nitrate, *oxide*, and sulfate)
Copper (*carbonate*, oxide red, *oxide black*, phosphate)
Crocus martis (red and yellow)
Ilmenite (*granular* and powder)
Iron (chromate, *oxide black*, *oxide red*, granular, and sulfate)
Manganese (*carbonate*, *dioxide*, granular, and sulfate)
Molybdenum oxide
Nickel (*oxide green* and oxide black)
Ochre, yellow
Opax
Potassium bichromate
Rutile
Selenium
Sienna (burnt and raw)

Tin oxide
Umber (burnt and raw)
Uranium oxide
Vanadium oxide
Zinc oxide
Zircon
Zircopax

Color in glazes is a very significant property and is affected by many factors. The color of the clay affects the color of the glaze, for if a clay burns to a white or light cream, it causes the glaze color to be brighter than if the clay were dark red or brown. The interior color of a fired piece (like a bowl), may be different from that of the exterior, because it is protected from the flame or oxidation conditions of the kiln's atmosphere. Coarse colorants, such as ilmenite, granular iron, and granular manganese, in the clay body will often break through the glaze surface to cause spotting or running streaks (this is often a desirable characteristic of stoneware). The atmosphere character will have a major effect on certain colorants: iron oxide in oxidation is slight buff, and in reduction becomes celedon; copper oxide in oxidation is a slight green color, and in reduction turns to blood red; chrome in oxidation is red at low temperatures; in reduction heavy raku has a silverlike color, and at stoneware temperatures is green.

The chart that follows is a suggestion of the possible colorants, their percentages, and the resulting fired color. Five glazes were used in the temperature range of C/012, C/02, C/2, C/6, and C/9 reduction. These glazes include low-lead, colemanite, high-lead, potash, and spodumene glaze types. More than twenty colorants were tested, and some of them are not commonly used. The percentages listed are a guide and should be tested in the individual glaze before using. As the chart illustrates, some colorants have different colors because of many variables.

GLAZE COLORANT CHART

Colorant	Percentage	Low-Lead Glaze C/012	Colemanite Glaze C/02	High-Lead Glaze C/2	Potash Glaze C/6	Spodumene Glaze C/9R
Antimony	4.0	Yellow (11)	Grayed yellow (12)	White (32)	Off-white (31)	Gray (103)
Antimony Burnt umber	8.0 4.0	Yellow (9) Brown (35)	Cream (14) Tan (18)	White (32) Tan (28)	Off-white (63) Brown (17)	Gray (103) Grayed brown (158)
Cadmium sulfide	2.0	Light yellow (3)	White (6)	White (32)	White (32)	Broken pink (48)
Cadmium sulfide	5.0	Yellow (1)	White (6), traces of pink	White (32)	White (32)	Broken pink (48)
Cerium	4.0	Orange (grayed 72)	Off-white (30)	White (7)	Off-white (6)	Gray (104)
Cerium	8.0	Orange-red (grayed 71)	Buff (40)	Off-white (31)	White (7)	Broken gray (103)
Chrome oxide green	2.0	Brilliant orange (69)	Chrome green (129)	Gray (104)	Warm gray (warm 104)	Gray (dark 115)
Cobalt oxide	.5	Blue-green (97)	Blue-purple (119)	Blue (93)	Blue (90)	Broken gray (103)
Copper oxide	.5	Chartreuse (125)	Light blue (86)	Light blue (86)	Light blue (86)	Broken gray (103)
Copper oxide	3.0	Green (123)	Blue-green (97)	Blue (84)	Gray (116)	Broken gray (104)
Copper phosphate	1.0	Chartreuse (126)	Light blue (86)	Light blue (86)	Blue (84)	Broken blue-gray (96)

Colorant	Percentage	Low-Lead Glaze C/012	Colemanite Glaze C/02	High-Lead Glaze C/2	Potash Glaze C/6	Spodumene Glaze C/9R
Copper phosphate	3.0	Green (122)	Blue (84)	Blue (86)	Blue-green (97)	Broken blue-gray (96)
Crocus martis	1.0	Yellow (13)	Buff (15)	Buff (30)	Tan (29)	Broken tan (23)
Crocus martis	3.0	Orange (57)	Tan (22)	Tan (29)	Yellow-brown (17)	Gray brown (146)
Ilmenite	1.0	Yellow (10)	Off-white (31)	White (7)	Spotted white (7)	Broken buff (23)
Iron chromate	1.0	Brilliant orange (72)	Gray (100)	Purple (109)	Gray (104)	Broken gray (103)
Iron chromate	4.0	Yellow (11)	Gray (115)	Purple (117)	Tan (146)	Broken tan (157)
Iron oxide, black	4.0	Yellow (13)	Tan (18)	Gray (103)	Yellow-brown (17)	Brown (155)
Iron oxide, red	10.0	Broken black (145)	Red-brown (74)	Dark gray (114)	Yellow-brown (dark 158)	Brown-black (dark 155)
Manganese dioxide	3.0	Brown-black (155)	Purple (107)	Gray-purple (120)	Grayed-purple (grayed 109)	Broken gray (103)
Molybdenum	4.0	Yellow (3)	White (15)	White (32)	Slight green (136)	Broken gray (103)
Molybdenum	8.0	Yellow (2)	Off-white (31)	White (7)	White (7)	Gray (96)
Nickel oxide, green	2.0	Yellow (1)	Tan (39)	Buff (29)	Gray (104)	Broken gray (103)
Opax	5.0	Yellow (13)	Off-white (7)	White (32)	Off-white (63)	Off-white (8)

Colorant	Percentage	Low-Lead Glaze C/012	Colemanite Glaze C/02	High-Lead Glaze C/2	Potash Glaze C/6	Spodumene Glaze C/9R
Potassium bichromate	2.0	Brilliant orange-red (70)	Grayed yellow (grayed 13)	Light purple (109)	Gray (151)	Broken gray (103)
Potassium bichromate	5.0	Orange (72)	Grayed yellow (17)	Light purple (109)	Off-white (30)	Broken tan (23)
Rutile	5.0	Yellow (2)	Pink (44)	Broken white (6)	Light orange (62)	Broken gray (151)
Selenium	2.0	Yellow-orange (10)	White (32)	White (32)	White (32)	Broken gray (103)
Selenium	5.0	Orange (38)	White (63)	White (32)	White (32)	Broken gray (103)
Sienna, burnt	2.0	Tan (13)	Off-white (29)	Off-white (31)	Tan (28)	Broken Tan (23)
Tin oxide	4.0	Cream (14)	Off-white (63)	Off-white (63)	Off-white (63)	Gray (104)
Umber, burnt	3.0	Brown (35)	Tan (27)	Off-white (8)	Tan (28)	Broken tan (22)
Uranium oxide	2.0	Orange (57)	Off-white (15)	Light yellow (5)	Yellow (3)	Broken gray (103)
Uranium oxide	6.0	Orange (72)	Buff (24)	Slight yellow (5)	Yellow-green (148)	Broken yellow-gray (101)
Vanadium	4.0	Orange-red (67)	Off-white (30)	Off-white (63)	White (31)	Yellow-gray (101)
Yellow ochre	2.0	Brilliant orange (72)	White (6)	White (7)	Off-white (30)	Broken gray (103)
Yellow ochre	5.0	Brilliant orange (72)	Buff (29)	White (8)	Tan (29)	Broken tan (23)
Zinc oxide	5.0	Yellow (11)	Off-white (63)	White (32)	Broken white (7)	Gray (103)

Colorant	Percentage	Low-Lead Glaze C/02	Colemanite Glaze C/02	High-Lead Glaze C/2	Potash Glaze C/6	Spodumene Glaze C/9R
Potassium bichromate	2.0 }			Blue (82)		
Copper oxide	3.0 }					
Selenium	5.0 }			White (32)		
Tin oxide	4.0 }					
Cobalt oxide	.5 }				Charcoal (116)	
Iron chromate	4.0 }					
Copper oxide	3.0 }				Gray (116)	
Manganese dioxide	3.0 }					
Selenium	2.0 }				Yellow (grayed 2)	
Uranium oxide	6.0 }					
Cadmium sulfide	2.0 }				Buff (29)	
Rutile	5.0 }					
Chrome oxide, green	2.0 }				Gray (101)	
Tin oxide	4.0 }					
Chrome oxide, green	2.0 }					Brown (155)
Copper phosphate	1.0 }					
Cadmium sulfide	5.0 }					Buff (31)
Cerium	8.0 }					
Uranium oxide	6.0 }					Gray (101)
Vanadium	4.0 }					
Iron oxide red	10.0 }					Brown (153)
Molybdenum	8.0 }					
Antimony	8.0 }					Gray (103)
Selenium	5.0 }					

Colorant	Percentage	Low-Lead Glaze C/012	Colemanite Glaze C/02	High-Lead Glaze C/2	Potash Glaze C/6	Spodumene Glaze C/9R
Zircopax	5.0	Yellow (3)	Off-white (63)	White (32)	White (32)	Gray (103)
Copper phosphate	3.0 ⎱	Blue (93)				
Cobalt oxide	.5 ⎰					
Cadmium sulfide	5.0 ⎱	Yellow-green (dark 125)				
Potassium bichromate	5.0 ⎰					
Yellow ochre	5.0 ⎱	Brown (156)				
Chrome oxide, green	2.0 ⎰					
Selenium	2.0 ⎱	Broken yellow (24)				
Crocus martis	3.0 ⎰					
Cadmium sulfide	5.0 ⎱		Yellow (24)			
Rutile	5.0 ⎰					
Copper phosphate	1.0 ⎱		Green (140)			
Uranium oxide	6.0 ⎰					
Copper phosphate	3.0 ⎱		Brown (137)			
Chrome oxide, green	2.0 ⎰					
Potassium bichromate	5.0 ⎱		Buff (29)			
Opax	5.0 ⎰					
Chrome oxide, green	2.0 ⎱			Blue (91)		
Cobalt oxide	.5 ⎰					
Copper phosphate	1.0 ⎱			Pale blue (86)		
Rutile	5.0 ⎰					

III

Enamel Formulas

The earliest known use of enamel dates from about the thirteenth century B.C. Gold rings with enamel from that period were discovered in a Mycenaean tomb at Koklia, Cypress. Later, Greeks in the fifth century B.C. used the cloisonné technique, and early Britons (first century B.C.) used the champlevé technique. The early phase of the Japanese Imari period of production, which extended to the end of the seventeenth century, is known for its lavish and gorgeous enamel-covered ceramics. Even though the clay was somewhat coarse during this period, the porcelains were highly embellished and splendiferous. The surface enrichment included designs from textile patterns, copies of Chinese models, and scenes ranging from daily Japanese life to exotic costumes. These ceramics were, for the most part, blue and white and/or decorated with enamels. Red enamel was the most predominant color, with black, blue, green, purple, gold, yellow, and silver colors. These enameled procelains are known as "Nishikide." Many tints, shades, and tones of enamel colors were finely ground, then painted on the porcelain, like water colors. The skills acquired in making a variety of enamel colors made possible refined and elegant enamel decorations.

The term "enamel" is also used for enamel paint, which makes for confusion; thus, the terms "jewelry enamel," "porcelain enamel," "baked enamel," and "copper enamel." In this book, enamel refers to heat-fused enamel. Various enamels are made transparent, opaque, hard-firing, soft-firing, flux (clear), fluoride, acid-resistant, leadless, low-lead, and very-low-temperature-firing for aluminum metal. Many very good commercial enamels of various colors and types are available and these are easy to use and reasonably priced. But to make one's own enamels is quite rewarding, for the enamelist then has a chance to experiment and formulate different colors. Unfortunately, the intricate computing of enamel calculations, the process of firing, grinding, washing, regrinding, and following through the problems involved in making individual enamels is often tedious. Formulation of new and old formulas and their recalculation will be necessary before the enamelist obtains satisfactory results and control over the process used. This arduous work, however, will result in a unique enamel, and this is what it is all about.

Testing and Formation Process

The enamelist preparing to create an enamel usually has the desired properties of that enamel in mind. To obtain the enamel that has the desired properties will necessitate a testing sequence to analyze the formula or formulas for the following characteristics:
1. ability of the base metal or clay to hold the fused enamel
2. fusion of the enamel to the metal or clay base
3. enamel retention of a smooth surface
4. degree of transparency of the enamel over the base
5. color of the enamel
6. bubbles in the enamel
7. enamel surface quality

The following testing sequence and production procedure can be used for testing enamels or for production of large amounts of enamel. The production of enamel is almost as complicated a process as the making of stains. The chemicals are weighed out in 100-gram units, dry-mixed, screened through a 120-mesh screen, and placed in a crucible. The crucible is placed in a kiln and fired to the suggested temperature, usually until all the bubbles are burned out and the mixture is in a fluid glassy state. At this point, the hot crucible is removed from the kiln with tongs and the fluid mixture is poured into cold water. In the water the hot fluid shatters into small pieces. Next, large lumps are broken up in a mortar, and the entire material is placed into a ball mill and ground, washed, and reground to a fine consistency. Certain enamels, especially those that use chrome, potassium bichromate, and cadmium sulfide, contain soluble materials and dissolved gases; to remove these requires refiring the enamel and repeating the grinding process. This ground mixture is sifted through an 80- or 100-mesh screen. For painting, silk-screening, or spraying, the enamels demand further grinding to pass through a 220- or finer mesh screen. Upon drying, the enamel is ready to apply to the surface of metal or clay. The powdered enamel is sifted upon a cleaned form (the most commonly used metals are copper and silver). This form is placed in a hot kiln and fired until the enamel forms a smooth surface. The temperature range of the kiln is 1500° to 1650° F., at which most enamels will melt, fuse to the surface, and form a smooth gloss surface. The hot enameled form is removed from the kiln and air-cooled.

Findings

The qualities desired for each enamel are determined by the enamel composition, colorants and their percentages, and the firing of the enamel over a white or flux (clear) coating on the base shape. Many of the colored transparents are more brilliant over a white enameled base. The information gained from each enamel test will help determine the alteration of the enamel formula or whether change in the percentage of colorants is necessary. The various data on each enamel formula are charted with each formula listed in the book. The translation of the information is explained in Figure 8.

Figure 8

Example of Enamel Formula with
Explanation of Related Data

E 4° Flux and Base for Colors

White lead	49†	Surface	Gloss	(The surface quality of the enamel)
Cullet	41	Fusion	Good	(The ability of the base to hold the enamel and the fusion of the enamel)
Kentucky ball #4	5	Flow	Smooth	(The enamel has a sufficient flow to form a smooth, even coating)
Whiting	5	Opacity	Clear	(The degree of transparency of the enamel over the base)
	———	Bubbles	None	(The amount of bubbles forming in the enameled surface)
	100	Color	Clear	(Enamel color)

Note: Dry mix, bisque @ C/4, wet grind, dry, screen 100 mesh (information on how to process the enamel)

°Number used for organization and identification.
†Percentage by weight

The formulas that follow are organized into clear, white, and colored groupings.

Enamel Formulas

E 1 Clear and Base for Colored Enamels

Potassium nitrate	54	Surface	Gloss
Red lead	28	Fusion	Good
Flint	18	Flow	Smooth
	———	Opacity	Transparent
	100	Bubbles	None
		Color	Clear (slight yellow 16)

Note: Dry-mix, bisque-fire @ C/6, wet-grind, dry, screen 100-mesh

E 2 Clear Flux

Red lead	50.4	Surface	Gloss
Boric acid	22.0	Fusion	Good
Flint	16.4	Flow	Smooth
Sodium nitrate	11.2	Opacity	Transparent
	———	Bubbles	None
	100.0	Color	Clear

Note: Dry-mix, bisque-fire @ C/5, wet-grind, dry, screen 100-mesh

E 3 Clear Flux

Red lead	50	Surface	Gloss
Borax	33	Fusion	Good
Silica	17	Flow	Smooth
	———	Opacity	Transparent
	100	Bubbles	None
		Color	Clear

Note: Dry-mix, bisque-fire until bubbles are gone and fluid, wet-grind, dry, screen 100-mesh

E 4 Enamel Flux

White lead	49	Surface	Gloss
Cullet	41	Fusion	Good
Kentucky ball #4	5	Flow	Smooth
Whiting	5	Opacity	Transparent
	———	Bubbles	None
	100	Color	Clear

Note: Dry-mix, bisque-fire @ C/6, wet-grind, dry, screen 100-mesh

E 5 Clear

Potassium nitrate	36	Surface	Gloss
Red lead	35	Fusion	Good
Flint	19	Flow	Smooth
Borax	5	Opacity	Transparent
Boric acid	5	Bubbles	None
	———	Color	Clear
	100		

Note: Dry-mix, bisque-fire @ C/4, wet-grind, dry, screen 100-mesh

E 6 Flux and Base for Colorants

Borax	29	Surface		Gloss
Flint	28	Fusion		Good
Soda feldspar	14	Flow		Smooth
Soda ash	10	Opacity		Transparent
Fluorspar	7	Bubbles		None
Cryolite	7	Color		Clear
Soda nitre	5			
	100			

Note: Dry-mix, bisque-fire @ C/6, wet-grind, dry, screen 100-mesh

E 7 Translucent White

Frit #W-18	74	Surface	Gloss
Tin oxide	15	Fusion	Smooth
China clay	11	Flow	Smooth
	——	Opacity	Translucent, thin
	100	Bubbles	None
		Color	Off-white (16)

Note: Dry-mix, bisque-fire @ C/6, wet-grind, dry, screen 100-mesh

E 8 White

Cullet	65	Surface	Gloss
Red lead	16	Fusion	Good
Tin oxide	6	Flow	Smooth
Potassium nitrate	6	Opacity	Opaque
Flint	5	Bubbles	None
Zircopax	2	Color	White (7)
	100		

Note: Dry-mix, bisque-fire @ C/6, wet-grind, dry, screen 100-mesh

E 9 White

White lead	54.7	Surface	Gloss
Flint	30.7	Fusion	Good
Potassium nitrate	5.2	Flow	Smooth
Tin oxide	4.6	Opacity	Opaque
Pearl ash	2.0	Bubbles	None
Soda ash	1.7	Color	White (6)
Soda feldspar	1.1		
	100.0		

Note: Dry-mix, bisque-fire @ C/4, wet-grind, dry, screen 100-mesh

E 10 White-yellow

White lead	51.5	Surface	Gloss
Flint	26.6	Fusion	Good
Cryolite	6.7	Flow	Smooth
Arsenic oxide	4.9	Opacity	Opaque
Potassium carbonate	4.4	Bubbles	None
Soda ash	3.8	Color	Yellow-white (5)
Potassium nitrate	2.1		
	100.0		

Note: Dry-mix, bisque-fire @ C/5, wet-grind, dry, screen 100-mesh

E 11 Yellow-amber

Red lead	48	Surface	Gloss
Borax	32	Fusion	Good
Flint	16	Flow	Smooth
Uranium oxide	4	Opacity	Transparent
		Bubbles	None
	100	Color	Yellow (2)

Note: Dry-mix, bisque-fire @ C/4, wet-grind, dry, screen 100-mesh

E 12 Yellow-white

Red lead	45.9	Surface	Gloss
Silica	21.6	Fusion	Good
Cullet	21.4	Flow	Smooth
Borax	5.4	Opacity	Translucent
Arsenic oxide	3.5	Bubbles	None
Potassium nitrate	2.0	Color	Yellow-white (5)
Sulfur	.2		
	100.0		

Note: Dry-mix, bisque-fire @ C/5, wet-grind, dry, screen 100-mesh

E 13 Pink

Red lead	52.9	Surface	Gloss
Silica	17.6	Fusion	Good
Cullet	16.1	Flow	Smooth
Pink stain	11.9	Opacity	Opaque
Boric acid	1.5	Bubbles	None
		Color	Pink (45)
	100.0		

Note: Color depends upon the pink stain used. Dry-mix, bisque-fire @ C/6, wet-grind, dry, screen 100-mesh

E 14 Amber

Red lead	55.3	Surface	Gloss
Flint	18.6	Fusion	Good
Cullet	12.5	Flow	Smooth
Uranium oxide	11.9	Opacity	Transparent
Soda ash	1.7	Bubbles	None
		Color	Amber (19)
	100.0		

Note: Dry-mix, bisque-fire @ C/5, wet-grind, dry, screen 100-mesh

E 15 Black

Red lead	54	Surface	Gloss
Cullet	18	Fusion	Good
Calcined borax	9	Flow	Smooth
Red iron oxide	8	Opacity	Opaque
Cobalt carbonate	7	Bubbles	None
Manganese dioxide	4	Color	Black (113)
	100		

Note: Dry-mix, bisque-fire @ C/6, wet-grind, dry, screen 100-mesh

Enamel Colorants

Colorants added to enamels extend the range of color possibilities. Since enamels are fired at lower temperature ranges, almost all colors are possible. But to achieve them requires the utmost care, otherwise the jewellike quality of the enamel will not be achieved. Most important, any impurity must be kept from mixing with the enamel; impurities show up as dirty marks in the finished product. The composition of enamel affects the color through a chemical reaction with the colorants. For instance, when the colorants selenium or antimony are used in some lead-bearing enamels, the result is a dirty brown color. Some colorants are affected in the presence of each other, such as nickel and manganese. The atmosphere character of the enamel melt, length of melt, and the melting temperature make it difficult to achieve true red, orange, and yellow colors, but not impossible.

The following chart is a suggestion of the possible colorants, their percentages, and the resulting fired color. The base enamels that were used are transparent E 8 and opaque E 1. Several colorants and colorant combinations were used. For other colors, commercial or individually formulated stains may be used. In some cases the use of stains is the only way certain red, orange, blue, and other colors can be achieved. The percentages listed are a guide and should be tested in the individual enamels before using.

Enamel Colorants Chart

		Resulting Color	
Colorant	*Per-centage*	*Enamel #N-1 (transparent base)*	*Enamel #N-8 (opaque base)*
Antimony oxide ⎱ Tin oxide ⎰	3.0 1.6	____	Translucent yellow-green (126)
Cadmium	3.0	Green (127)	Opaque gray-white (7)
Cadmium Antimony Red iron oxide	5.0 ⎫ 2.5 ⎬ .8 ⎭	____	Opalescence, yellow-white (15)

Resulting Color

Colorant	Per-centage	Enamel N-1 (transparent base)	Enamel N-8 (opaque base)
Cadmium Selenium	2.4 1.2	Green (126)	Slight opalescence, whitish
Chrome oxide green	2.0	Yellow-green (light 144)	Translucent green (141)
Chrome oxide green Manganese dioxide	2.0 3.0	——	Translucent purple (117)
Chrome oxide green Nickel oxide green	3.0 1.5	——	Translucent green (139)
Cobalt oxide	1.0	Blue (93)	Translucent bright blue (bright 93)
Cobalt oxide Zinc oxide	1.0 6.0	Blue (93)	Translucent blue (92)
Copper oxide	.8	Green (131)	Translucent blue (83)
Copper phosphate	3.0	Blue-green (86)	
Copper phosphate Uranium	3.0 6.0	Blue-green (84)	Translucent green (121)
Manganese carbonate Red iron oxide Cobalt oxide Chrome oxide green	1.0 1.0 1.0 1.0	Opaque blue-black (89-113)	Opaque blue-black (89-113)
Opax	8.0	——	Translucent white (6)
Potassium bichromate	3.0	Yellow-green (brilliant 144)	Opaque green (141)
Potassium bichromate Cobalt oxide	3.6 .6	Green (129)	Translucent green (129)
Potassium bichromate Copper carbonate	1.2 .8	Green (125)	Translucent green (144)

Resulting Color

Colorant	Per-centage	Enamel N-1 (transparent base)	Enamel N-8 (opaque base)
Red iron oxide	1.8	Yellow-amber (142)	—
Red iron oxide Potassium bichromate	1.6 2.6	Yellow-amber (142)	—
Selenium	6.0	—	Translucent whitish
Tin oxide	6.0	No change	Opaque white (6)
Umber, burnt	3.0	Brown (156)	Translucent tan (159)
Uranium	6.0	Yellow (3)	Translucent yellow (11)
Vanadium	4.0	Greenish (126)	Translucent greenish (126-144)

IV

Glass Formulas

Man very likely first made glass on the banks of the River Belus in Syria when travelers used some natron rocks, probably ones they were transporting, as supports for their cooking. The fire's heat fused the soda-bearing rock and sand into glass. This legend accounts for the first man-made glass, but the first manufacturing of glass has been traced to Mesopotamia and Egypt. It is believed that before 300 B.C., glass was made into beads and small pieces for jewelry and other decorations. The Egyptians developed the sandcore glass, and the Syrians, perhaps, invented the blowpipe to make "blown glass."

Many different cultures of varying periods made glass, some more decorative or ornate than others. "Contemporary" glass, with its ultra-simple form, contains little or no decoration; the clarity of this glass, its clean lines, and graceful forms are its predominant attractions. One of the earliest contemporary designs can be traced to Sweden: known as "juno," it was tableware cut in a parallel-rib pattern from the Kosta Glass Works, *circa* 1890. Most of the demand for glassware in this period was for the cut, etched, cameo, painted, and ornamented type, and many of the Swedish glass craftsmen produced the then popular Belgian and French designs. A few, however, started what is known as "Contemporary Swedish Design" after the depression of the 1880s, when glass production was extended. (A notable glass craftsman was Simon Gate, who worked at Orrefors Glassworks.) The Swedish design spread as the result of the Gothenburg Exposition of 1923. An exhibit of Swedish crafts was held in 1927 at the Metropolitan Museum of Art in New York City; it became popular, went to Chicago and then Detroit. Thus the promotion of Sweden's glass promoted several other Swedish glass works to develop their own version of "Swedish Glass" as it is known today. By the 1930s Swedish glass had arrived when the Swedish pavilion displayed glass and crafts during the New York World's Fair, 1939-40, at which the Swedish design was acclaimed for its function, beauty, and grace. The glass became internationally known during the early 1940s and still holds it's place today.*

Form follows function, a creative ideal which is associated with Frank Lloyd Wright, along with the ideals and concepts of pre-Nazi German Bauhaus and the search for beauty, has influenced all aspects of crafts. The rise of individually shaped glass forms as a creative expression started in the 1950s in the United States with one or two craftsmen. Today there are several glass craftsmen and many universities and colleges are offering glass courses and even grant degrees in glasscraft. The study of glass itself, that is, technical understanding, is fascinating, and the possible uses of glass seem unlimited. Technically speaking, glass can be defined as "an inorganic product of fusion which has been cooled to a rigid condition without crystallization."† Many different types of glass are available and are used for various products. Some of the various glass types are container flint, container amber, window green, window, plate, opal jar, opal, illumination, ruby selenium, ruby borosilicate, fiber-glass, lead tableware, technical, lamp bulb, heat-absorbing, borosilicate crown, specticle, optical flint, Pyrex, thermometer, high-lead, and soda lime. The number of types illustrates that the science of glass composition and glass colors is one of the

---

*Elisa Steenberg, *Swedish Glass* (New York: Gramercy Publishing Company, 1950).

†*ASTM Standards of Glass and Glass Products,* prepared by ASTM committee C14, American Society for Testing Materials, April 1955.

most important aspects of glass-making. By taking advantage of the various technical books and available formulas, many exciting results can be obtained. The basic composition of glass is important in controlling workability and color, in some cases it is critical for obtaining certain red and orange colors. Unusual and subtle colors are not overly difficult if some time is spent testing the various formulas, cullet (ground window or other glass), and marbles (used in the making of fiberglass) that are available and used for glass-making.

The art of glass-making is hot and dirty; it uses much expensive equipment and tools; it requires patience and manual dexterity and a knowledge of glass chemistry. However, the rewards are worth the effort. Many colleges and glass craftsmen use cullet or marbles as the mainstay of their glass-making, adding various colorants. The advantage of marbles and cullet is that they do not give off as noxious fumes as do melting raw materials; and the cost of marbles is about $220 a ton. To determine the individual properties of the various glass formulas, cullet, or marbles that would come closest to the desired properties requires testing under the actual conditions.

Testing

There are over twenty different types of mass-produced commercial glass with an unknown number of specialty glasses. Even so, the types of glass for hand-blowing are limited. An ideal glass would have the following qualities:

1. The glass cools slowly, due to heat radiation, during the working of the glass.
2. The viscosity of the glass is high at a low working temperature range.
3. The glass has a high degree of "workability."
4. The melted glass rapidly becomes virtually free of bubbles in the melt (fining).
5. The glass has an extensive color range.
6. The glass is susceptible to a low stress level and anneals easily.

No known glass has all of the desired qualities, but a few have most of them. The soft borosilicate glass has a low working temperature range and a reasonable working time. However, the cool glass will require reheating before hot glass is added to prevent cracking due to incompatible expansion. Several glass formulas have most of the qualities for hand-blowing.

The formulas were put to a uniform testing sequence and procedure that provided the necessary information about the glass. All formulas, cullets, or marbles were measured into 100-gram batches, dry-mixed, and placed in a clay crucible. The crucible was placed in a kiln and fired until fluid and the bubbles fined out. The kiln was turned off and the glass cooled, the glass was analyzed for its ability to fine rapidly the bubbles, color, and the temperature fired.

Findings

The qualities desired for glass are determined by the workability, temperature range melt of the glass, glass composition, the use of the finished product, and the techniques used to make the glass product. The information gained from the testing will help determine whether the addition or subtraction of the various possible ingredients to the glass formulas is necessary. For example, the workability of cullet is short and the temperature-time range is limited. The addition of soda ash, sodium bicarbonate, or potassium nitrate will improve this glass. The color of fiber-glass marbles is pale green, and to decolor the glass a very small amount of selenium is used.

The various data for each glass formula are charted with each formula listed in the book. The formulas are organized into clear, white, and colored groups. The translation of the information is explained in Figure 9.

Figure 9

Example of a Glass Formula with
Explanation of Related Data

GS 10° Amber

Sand	64.1†	Fining	Good	(The amount of bubbles and stones, etc., in the melted batch)
Soda ash	22.4	Temperature	C/9R	(The temperature and kiln character of the glass melt)
Whiting	12.8	Opacity	Clear	(The degree of transparency of the glass)
Carbon	.4	Color	Amber (40)	(The color and the color code number)
Sulfur	.3			
	100.0			

Note: (Any additional information)

° Glaze number used for organization and identification.
† Percentage by weight.

Glass Formulas

GS 1 Cullet

Cullet	100	Fining	Good
		Temperature fired	C/9R
		Opacity	Transparent
		Color	Clear

GS 2 Marbles

Marbles	100	Fining	Good
		Temperature fired	C/9R
		Opacity	Transparent
		Color	Clear, slight amber

GS 3 Clear

Cullet	75.5	Fining	Good
Flint	12.2	Temperature fired	C/9R
Potash feldspar	7.2	Opacity	Transparent
Borax	3.3	Color	Clear
Tin oxide	1.4		
Arsenious oxide	.3		
	99.9		

GS 4 Flint, Soda Ash, Clear

Flint	47.0	Fining	Good
Soda ash	29.5	Temperature fired	C/9R
Cryolite	10.5	Opacity	Transparent
Barium carbonate	5.5	Color	Clear
Potash	5.0		
Potassium nitrate	1.5		
Zinc oxide	1.0		
	100.0		

GS 5 Soda Ash, Clear

Flint	47	Fining	Good
Soda ash	28	Temperature fired	C/9R
Potassium nitrate	8	Opacity	Transparent
Barium carbonate	5	Color	Clear
Borax	5		
Cryolite	3		
Zinc oxide	2		
Dolomite	2		
	100		

GS 6 Flint, Whiting, Clear

Flint	38.62	Fining	Very good
Whiting	22.53	Temperature fired	C/9R
Boric acid	21.26	Opacity	Transparent
Alumina	10.27	Color	Clear
Manganese carbonate	6.24		
Soda ash	1.08		
	100.00		

GS 7 Opal

Flint	40.9	Fining	Good
Soda feldspar	24.5	Temperature fired	C/9R
Soda ash	17.4	Opacity	Clear to slight opal
Fluorspar	7.4	Color	Off-white (16)
Sodium silica fluoride	7.4		
Zinc oxide	1.6		
Cadmium sulfide	.8		
	100.0		

GS 8 Yellow

Soda ash	38.0	Fining	Good
Flint	25.3	Temperature fired	C/9R
Lime	25.3	Opacity	Translucent
Borax	5.1	Color	Yellow-white (5)
Cadmium sulfide	.8		
Sulfur	1.2		

100.0

GS 9 Amber

Soda ash	37.9	Fining	Good
Lime	28.5	Temperature fired	C/9R
Sand	15.8	Opacity	Clear
Cryolite	7.9	Color	Amber (13)
Fluorspar	7.9		
Sulfur	2.0		

100.0

GS 10 Amber

Sand	64.1	Fining	Good
Soda ash	22.4	Temperature fired	C/9R
Limespar	12.8	Opacity	Clear
Carbon	.4	Color	Amber (40)
Sulfur	.3		

100.0

GS 11 Amber

Flint	64.7	Fining	Good
Soda ash	19.8	Temperature fired	C/9R
Whiting	14.2	Opacity	Clear
Sodium sulfate	.9	Color	Amber (29)
Carbon	.3		
Sulfur	.1		

100.0

GS 12 Copper Ruby Red

Flint	50.00	Fining	Good
Lithium carbonate	40.00	Temperature fired	C/9R
Alumina	9.79	Opacity	Clear
Tin oxide	.20	Color	Slight green (133)
Copper oxide	.01	Note: Ruby red when struck	

100.00

GS 13 Cadmium Red Ruby

Flint	63.2	Fining	Good
Soda ash	22.1	Temperature fired	C/9R
Potash	6.3	Opacity	Clear
Whiting	3.2	Color	Clear
Borax	3.2	Note: Red when struck	
Bone ash	1.2		
Cadmium sulfide	.5		
Selenium	.2		
Sulfur	.1		

100.0

GS 14 Selenium Ruby

Silica	56.9	Fining	Good
Sodium carbonate	21.2	Temperature fired	C/9R
Zinc oxide	8.5	Opacity	Clear
Borax	4.6	Color	Clear
Cryolite	2.3	Note: Red when struck	
Cadmium sulfide	2.0		
Potassium carbonate	1.7		
Bone ash	1.1		
Selenium	1.1		
Sodium chloride	.6		
	100.0		

GS 15 Red Violet

Flint	50.1	Fining	Good
Red lead	31.1	Temperature fired	C/9R
Potash	15.0	Opacity	Clear
Potassium nitrate	2.5	Color	Red violet (bright 106)
Manganese dioxide	1.3		
	100.0		

GS 16 Red

Red lead	42.4	Fining	Good
Flint	38.5	Temperature fired	C/9R
Potassium carbonate	13.1	Opacity	Transparent, thin
Sodium carbonate	3.9		Opaque, thick
Manganese carbonate	1.9	Color	Purple where thin (118)
Copper carbonate	.2		Purple-black where thick
	100.0		

Note: Try gold (trichloride) .2 instead of copper for flash red (expensive)

GS 17 Dark Blue

Sand	49.20	Fining	Good
Red lead	33.40	Temperature fired	C/9R
Potassium carbonate	14.80	Opacity	Translucent, thin
Potassium nitrate	2.50		Opaque, thick
Cobalt oxide	.03	Color	Blue (93) where thin
			Blue-black (89) where thick
	100.03		

GS 18 Bright Blue

Sand	65.7	Fining	Good
Potassium carbonate	22.3	Temperature fired	C/9R
Whiting	11.2	Opacity	Transparent, thin
Tin oxide	.7		Opaque, thick
Cobalt oxide	.3	Color	Blue (light 89) where thin
	100.2		

GS 19 Dark Blue

Sand	66.5	Fining	Good
Potassium carbonate	22.6	Temperature	C/9R
Whiting	10.7	Opacity	Translucent, thin
Cobalt oxide	.4		Opaque, thick
		Color	Blue (89) where thin
	100.2		Blue (dark 89) where thick

Glass Colors

Colorants for glass are the same as those used for clays, glazes, enamels, and stains, and examples are indicated below. Enamel and glass colorants, perhaps the most delicate and sensitive of all ceramic colorants, are affected by temperature, glass composition, annealing, striking (reheating), atmosphere character of the glass melt and working flame, and the character of the colorants themselves. Certain copper glass compounds, under oxidation, reduction, heavy reduction, or striking condition, for example, could have a resulting color ranging from clear to pale green to red or to metallic copper surface. Most other colorants are not this complicated. But this points up the degree and significance of influences that colorants encounter.

The following chart is a suggestion of the possible colorants (as fired in a slightly reducing atmosphere), their percentages, and the resulting fired color. The base glass that was used is the fiber-glass formula No. GS 6, as this is one of the most commonly used types of glass. Several colorants and colorant combinations were used. The percentages listed are a guide and should be tested in the individual glass before using.

Glass Colorant Chart

Colorant	Percentage	Resulting Color
Red iron oxide	.2	Blue (93)
Selenium	.8	
Selenium	.6	Slight blue (88)
Red iron oxide	.1	
Arsenic	.6	
Selenium	6.0	Gray (8)
Selenium	4.0	Gray (8)
Uranium	8.0	Blue-black (113)
Selenium	2.0	

Glass Colorant Chart

Colorant	*Percentage*	*Resulting Color*
Selenium Cadmium sulfide	2.0⎫ 3.0⎭	Slight yellow (64)
Selenium Cadmium Zinc oxide	5.0⎫ 1.0⎬ 5.0⎭	Slight green (135)
Uranium	3.0	Blue (98)
Uranium	6.0	Blue-black (dark 92)
Cadmium sulfide Zinc oxide	4.0⎫ 3.0⎭	Milky, slight yellow (6)
Iron oxide	.6	Blue (85)
Iron oxide	3.0	Black where thick (113)
Cobalt carbonate Red iron oxide	.4⎫ .4⎭	Blue-black (89)
Manganese carbonate	.6	Gray (104)
Manganese carbonate Red iron oxide	.6⎫ .4⎭	Slight amber (29)
Manganese carbonate Copper carbonate	.4⎫ .2⎭	Slight brown (28)
Manganese carbonate	1.8	Slight amber (24)
Chrome oxide	.4	Chrome green (123)
Chrome oxide	1.0	Chrome green (dark 123)

Glass Colorant Chart

Colorant	Percentage	Resulting Color
Copper carbonate	.6	Slight green (135)
Vanadium	.4	Green (133)
Vanadium	1.0	Black where thick (129)
Copper carbonate Chrome oxide	.6 } .4 }	Green (124)7
Lead chromate	1.8	Green (131) plus marbled colors
Copper carbonate Red iron oxide	.6 } .4 }	Dark blue (90)
Copper carbonate Black iron oxide	1.9 } .4 }	Blue (90) plus red spots
Copper carbonate Chrome oxide	.6 } .4 }	Red brown (50)
Manganese dioxide Cobalt carbonate	.6 } .2 }	Blue (91)
Nickel carbonate	.6	Gray-brown (116)
Cerium Titanium Manganese	.8 } .8 } .6 }	Yellow (20)
Antimony Titanium	.8 } 1.6 }	Yellow (18)
Tin oxide	1.0	Clear

Glass Colorant Chart

Colorant	Percentage	Resulting Color
Tin oxide	3.0	Slight milky
Tin oxide	10.0	Milky (31)
Copper carbonate Tin oxide	.5 ⎫ 1.0 ⎬	Blood red (flashed 54)

Temperature Equivalents:
Orton Standard Pyrometric Cones°

Cone number	Large Cones†		Small Cones†	
	150°C	*270°F*	*300°C*	*540°F*
020	635	1175	666	1231
019	683	1261	723	1333
018	717	1323	752	1386
017	747	1377	784	1443
016	792	1458	825	1517
015	804	1479	843	1549
014	838	1540		
013	852	1566		
012	884	1623		
011	894	1641		
010	894	1641	919	1686
09	923	1693	955	1751
08	955	1751	983	1801
07	984	1803	1008	1846
06	999	1830	1023	1873
05	1046	1915	1062	1944
04	1060	1940	1098	2008
03	1101	2014	1131	2068
02	1120	2048	1148	2098
01	1137	2079	1178	2152
1	1154	2109	1179	2154
2	1162	2124	1179	2154
3	1168	2134	1196	2185
4	1186	2167	1209	2208
5	1196	2185	1221	2230
6	1222	2232	1255	2291
7	1240	2264	1264	2307
8	1263	2305	1300	2372
9	1280	2336	1317	2403
10	1305	2381	1330	2426

Cone number	Large Cones†		Small Cones†	
	150°C	*270°F*	*300°C*	*540°F*
11	1315	2399	1336	2437
12	1326	2419	1335	2471
13	1346	2455		
14	1366	2491		
15	1431	2608		

*From the Edward Orton, Jr., Ceramic Foundation, Columbus, Ohio.
†Temperature rise per hour.

Bibliography of Suggested Readings

Andrews, Andrew I. *Porcelain Enamels*. Champaign, Ill.: The Garrard Press, 1961.

Binns, Charles. *The Potter's Craft*. Princeton, N.J.: D. Van Nostrand Company, 1967.

Colbeck, John. *Pottery: The Technique of Throwing*. New York: Watson-Guptill Publications, 1969.

Counts, Charles. *Pottery Workshop*. New York: Macmillan Publishing Co., Inc., 1973.

Kenny, J. B. *The Complete Book of Pottery Making*. New York: Greenberg, 1949.

Kingery, W. D. *Introduction to Ceramics*. New York: John Wiley and Sons, 1963.

Leach, Bernard. *A Potter's Book*. London: Faber and Faber, 1960.

Littleton, Harvey K. *Glassblowing: A Search for Form*. New York: Van Nostrand Reinhold Company, 1971.

Nelson, G. C. *Ceramics*. New York: Holt, Rinehart and Winston, Inc., 1960.

Norton, F. H. *Elements of Ceramics*. Reading, Mass.: Addison-Wesley Publishing Company, 1957.

Piepenburg, Robert. *Raku Pottery*. New York: Macmillan Publishing Co., Inc., 1972.

Riegger, Hal. *Raku Art and Technique*. New York: Van Nostrand Reinhold Company, 1970.

Rhodes, Daniel. *Clay and Glazes for the Potter*. New York: Chilton Company, 1959.

————. *Stoneware and Porcelain*. New York: Chilton Company, 1959.

NOTE: The above suggested readings are concerned with the how-to aspect of creating ceramic forms and related technical information.